50 LESSONS FOR HAPPY LAWYERS

OTHER BOOKS BY NORA RIVA BERGMAN

50 Lessons for Lawyers: Earn more. Stress less. Be awesome.

50 Lessons for Women Lawyers – From Women Lawyers
Career and Life Lessons from 50 Successful Women Lawyers

Available at amazon.com, Barnes & Noble, and as a Kindle book.

COMING SOON

50 Lessons for Young Lawyers

50 LESSONS FOR HAPPY LAWYERS

Boost wellness. Build resilience.
Yes, you can!

NORA RIVA BERGMAN, JD
and
CHELSY A. CASTRO, JD, MA, AM, LCSW

50 Lessons for Happy Lawyers

Boost wellness. Build resilience. Yes, you can!

50 Lessons for Happy Lawyers, its logo and marks are trademarks of Berroco Canyon Publishing.

Cover Design: CODESIGN – www.codesign.cc
Interior Design and Layout by Hudson Valley Book Design – www.hudsonvalleybookdesign.com
Editor: Michael Premo – www.613creativeinc.com

Berroco Canyon Publishing

ISBN: 978-0-9972637-4-9
ISBN: 978-0-9972637-5-6
Library of Congress Control Number: 2022907375
Berroco Canyon Publishing

TABLE OF CONTENTS

A NOTE FROM THE AUTHORS

We wrote this book because the legal profession is at an inflection point, and we believe that lawyers deserve to live happy, healthy, resilient lives. This book is designed to help lawyers do just that. If we can change how we work, we can change how we live—and vice versa.

As a profession that has historically resisted change, the legal profession has been forced to change almost overnight in response to the COVID-19 pandemic. While writing this book, we are cautiously optimistic that the end of the pandemic is in sight, and people everywhere are looking forward to returning to "normal." But do lawyers truly want to return to the way things were before the pandemic?

Prior to the pandemic, the 2016 study by the Hazelden Betty Ford Foundation and the American Bar Association Commission on Lawyer Assistance Programs, the first of its kind in decades, found that "21% of licensed, employed attorneys qualify as problem drinkers, 28% struggle with some level of depression and 19% demonstrate symptoms of anxiety." The 2018 Legal Trends Report stated, "75% of lawyers report frequently or always working outside of regular business hours, and that 39% of lawyers say these long hours negatively affect their personal lives." These statistics are the result of a culture that says, "Get to the office early, work late, and be sure to work on the weekends, too." Those are the behaviors that the profession has rewarded, and the results are now strikingly clear. We think there is a better way.

Some people will tell you that happiness is a choice. We disagree. It's not quite that simple. We have come to realize that happiness, like the law, is a practice. It is something we can cultivate—little by little and bit by bit—every day. While we cannot merely flip a switch and become happy, we can practice happiness. And practice makes permanent.

You may have already noticed that we've written this book using the pronoun "we." We chose this style for the seamless way it allows us to speak in a collective voice and in a way that takes advantage of our diverse backgrounds. Nora Bergman has practiced as a litigator and certified mediator. She has coached lawyers and law firms for over 15 years and worked with bar associations and legal aid organizations across the country. In addition to her law degree, Chelsy Castro holds a master's degree in clinical social work and has trained thousands of lawyers, judges, and law students in evidence-based stress management techniques. Prior to her psychotherapy practice, Chelsy was an attorney in international development and international regulatory compliance. We are lawyers who work with lawyers to help them achieve their goals, and we bring a different perspective to our work.

Finally, this book is written for individuals. While we touch on the topic of law firm culture in *Lesson 2*, the lessons in this book focus on what we can do, as individuals, to lead happier, healthier, more resilient lives. We realize we cannot change the profession, but we can provide scientifically sound strategies and suggestions to help you live a happier life. We can help you focus on your happiness and well-being, and you can be a role model for those around you. By doing so, you will not only improve your own life, but you will influence the lives of others. Gandhi said, "Be the change you wish to see in the world." We hope our book gives you the tools you need to be the change.

A portion of the proceeds from the sale of this book will benefit our partners, the Greater Good Science Center, the Anxiety and Depression Association of America, and the Institute for Well-Being in Law.

DISCLAIMER

This book is not intended to provide diagnosis, treatment, or medical advice. The content provided is for informational purposes only. This book is not a substitute for professional help if you are experiencing issues or challenges regarding your physical, mental, or emotional health. This book is designed to provide accurate and authoritative information with respect to the subject matter covered. It is sold with the understanding that neither the publisher nor the authors are engaged in rendering psychological, financial, legal, or other professional services. If expert assistance or counseling is needed, the services of a competent professional should be sought.

Many of the lessons in this book cite websites and other online resources. The authors have made every effort to provide accurate url addresses at the time of publication. However, url addresses can change over time, and the publisher does not have control of or responsibility for changes that occur after publication. Additionally, the publisher does not assume responsibility for the content of cited websites.

ACKNOWLEDGMENTS

Writing this book has been the definition of collaboration. This book would not have been possible without the efforts and talents of so many. We'd like to thank our editor, Michael Premo, for his commitment and thoughtful comments throughout the writing process; our website and cover designer, Brian Frolo of CoDesign, for his creativity and attention to detail; Glen Edelstein of Hudson Valley Book Design for his work on the interior design; and the team at Books Fluent and Books Forward for their direction and support throughout this project.

Special thanks to everyone who was interviewed and lent their voice to this book. Know that your insights informed many of the lessons and were invaluable.

FROM NORA

Thank you, also, to Trevor Crane and the team at Epic Author for their support at the inception of this project. Finally, thank you seems almost inadequate to convey my gratitude to Jan for her unconditional love and support throughout this process and always. And to my writing buddy, Quinn, who often slept under my desk as I worked and offered her editorial comments.

FROM CHELSY

Thank you to my ancestors whose life stories have taught me that the power to change our lives lies within each of us. Thank you to my wonderful husband, Brent, and to my loving daughters, Eva and Belen. Your support, love, and zest for life make every day a beautiful adventure.

HOW TO USE THIS BOOK

I've learned that I still have a lot to learn.

– *Maya Angelou*

50 Lessons for Happy Lawyers is the third book in the *50 Lessons for Lawyers* series. It's written for lawyers, but you don't have to be a lawyer to benefit from the lessons in this book. The lessons are essential for anyone who wants to live a happier, healthier, more resilient life. As you experiment with them, you'll begin to see your life change for the better.

The lessons in this book draw on dozens of other books, published scientific research, various online resources, and decades of professional experience. All books, research, and online resources are cited at the end of each lesson. We are indebted to the authors cited here for the lessons they have taught us through their research and writing. We recommend making the books we reference part of your happiness and wellness library.

This book can be explored in any way you like. You can read it from cover to cover, reading all of the lessons sequentially, or you can start with any lesson that resonates with you. You don't have to start with *Lesson 1*. However, we recommend it because *Lesson 1* provides the foundation for all the following lessons.

While all 50 lessons are important, some may be more relevant to you than others. Some lessons are longer than others and include multiple citations to other resources. Some lessons are shorter. The length of a lesson isn't an indication of its value or importance. Also, you'll notice that many of the lessons cite other lessons because they are relevant to the lesson you're reading, so it's okay to jump around if you want to. Regardless, each offers valuable happiness strategies that you can put to work right now.

You might want to use this book as your one-year course on well-being by reading (and applying!) one lesson each week over the course of a year. You may find that you want to spend more than one week on a particular lesson, and that's okay, too. Think of each lesson as a new habit and focus on creating that habit.

In the end, we retain from our studies only that which we practically apply.
– Goethe

One of the lessons from the first book in the *50 Lessons for Lawyers* series is: Understand the Difference Between Knowing and Doing. Start Doing. All too often, we confuse knowing with doing. Knowledge without action is meaningless. If we want to live happier lives, we must do something about it. As you'll learn in *Lesson 1*, we can have a tremendous impact on our level of happiness by simply doing those things that make us happy.

The importance of doing—taking action—is why each lesson ends with a section called Living the Lesson that provides suggestions on applying the lesson to your life and legal practice. Living the Lesson helps you move from knowing—to doing.

Finally, just a couple of notes on our writing style. We use the pronoun "they" as a singular nonbinary pronoun rather than "he or she." We have also chosen to hyphenate well-being, as this book follows the Chicago Manual of Style (17th edition). The manual hyphenates well-being; however, numerous resources we've cited don't hyphenate well-being. You will see both versions here. These are not typos but a conscious choice to not alter the original quotes.

Here's to the journey!

Nora Riva Bergman
nora@reallifepractice.com

Chelsy A. Castro
ccastro@castrojacobs.com

Lesson 1

LIKE THE LAW, HAPPINESS IS A PRACTICE.

I believe that the very purpose of our life is to seek happiness.

– *Dalai Lama*

At one time or another, we've all had the same thought. "I'll be happy when [fill in the blank]." For some reason, we have been conditioned to believe that happiness is the result of something happening to us or something we achieve. But that is not how happiness works. Or maybe we've been conditioned to believe that if we have a certain amount of money or a bigger house or a new car or a better job, then we will be happy. But that is also not how happiness works.

There are so many people who, by all outward appearances, should be happy. Yet on the inside, they are suffering. In the legal profession, the pain of unhappiness is almost endemic. Research has shown that attorneys experience depression at a higher rate than the general public. Given the stress that is so often part of the practice of law, it's not surprising that too many attorneys suffer from depression. If you are suffering from depression, this book is not a substitute for professional help. However, learning how to increase the happiness you experience—regardless of where you are in your life—can be invaluable.

WHAT IS HAPPINESS?

First, let's define happiness. According to the *Merriam-Webster Dictionary*, happiness is "a state of well-being and contentment." According to Sonja

Lyubomirsky, a professor in the Department of Psychology at the University of California, Riverside, happiness encompasses both positive emotions and a sense of satisfaction. So, let's go back to that definition. The truth is that while there may be common components of happiness, those components may differ from person-to-person.

In her book, *The How of Happiness: A Scientific Approach to Getting the Life You Want,*[1:1] Lyubomirsky shares her research on happiness and some of the myths around it. She notes three factors that determine our level of happiness: Set Point, Circumstances, and Intentional Activity. Our Set Point, which accounts for about 50 percent of our happiness, is rooted in our genetics. Circumstances—what happens to us—account for only about 10 percent of our happiness. The remaining 40 percent of our happiness in life is determined by our Intentional Activity. Yes, we can increase the level of happiness in our lives by intentionally doing those things that make us feel happy. So simple. Yet, simple doesn't necessarily mean easy. She describes her research based on studies of twins. We won't go into it here, but we highly recommend reading her book.

HAPPINESS IS NOT TOXIC POSITIVITY

Toxic positivity is defined as only focusing on positive things and rejecting anything that may trigger negative emotions. There is a difference between maintaining a positive mindset in the face of challenges and avoiding those challenges or pretending they don't exist. If there are weeds in your garden, a positive mindset doesn't tell you to just ignore them or pretend they are not there. If you have a positive mindset, you notice the weeds and get busy pulling them out. You have a mindset that says, "I see the weeds. I know they are not good for my garden. And I'm going to deal with them." Practicing happiness is not about denying or avoiding unpleasant emotions or circumstances, rather, it's about how we respond to those problems and challenges.

As you'll learn in the lesson on mindfulness, denying our emotions only makes them stronger. And, as you'll learn in the lesson on empathy, being able to feel what someone else is feeling can actually serve to increase your happiness and theirs. This may be particularly true when you can empathize with someone feeling painful emotions.

WHY PRACTICE HAPPINESS?

In Shawn Achor's book, *The Happiness Advantage: The Seven Principles of Positive Psychology That Fuel Success and Performance at Work,*[1:2] he shares research from numerous studies demonstrating that when we are happy and in a positive state of mind, we are better able to "make and sustain more neural connections, which allows us to think more quickly and creatively, become more skilled at complex analysis and problem solving and see and invent new ways of doing things."

The bottom line is that being happier will make you a better lawyer. Yet, when you think of your typical day, how often do you feel happy? How often do you feel positive emotions? The work lawyers do—identifying problems, spotting issues, playing out worst-case scenarios—can lead to an overdose of negative emotions, but your brain needs the exact opposite to be at its creative best.

> *Waiting to be happy limits our brain's potential for success, whereas cultivating positive brains makes us more motivated, efficient, resilient, creative, and productive, which drives performance upward.*
>
> – From *The Happiness Advantage*

In addition to making you a better lawyer, being happy has many other documented benefits. According to research from the Greater Good Center at UC Berkeley, happiness benefits your health in the following six very specific ways:[1:3]

- Happiness promotes lower heart rate and blood pressure.
- Happiness strengthens your immune system.
- Happiness can reduce stress.
- Happiness can help to reduce pain and inflammation.
- Happiness combats disease and disability.
- Happiness lengthens our lives.

HAPPINESS SUPPORTS WELLNESS AND CULTIVATES RESILIENCE

Happiness, wellness, and resilience all work together to enhance our quality of life. Each concept builds on and supports the others. Each concept *needs* the others, and we need all three to be at our best. While being healthy and physically well can certainly make you feel happy, it's also true that experiencing happiness can improve your health. And being happy—feeling positive emotions—can help us to be more resilient. We'll talk more about resilience in *Lesson 3*, but for now, just know that when we are resilient, we can bounce back more easily from difficult situations. Whether the difficult situation is a ruling you didn't expect in one of your cases, a challenge with a client, or a diagnosis you didn't expect from your doctor, our level of resilience makes all the difference in how we respond.

PRACTICE. PRACTICE. PRACTICE.

So, now you know what happiness is and why it's important for your work and your quality of life. Increasing your happiness is all about doing things that make you feel happy. We're not suggesting you can flip a switch and become happier. We are suggesting that small changes every day can make a big difference in how happy you feel. Just like the law, happiness is a practice. And while practice may not make perfect, it does make permanent.

> *If we observe genuinely happy people, we shall find that they do not just sit around being contented. They make things happen. They pursue new understandings, seek new achievements, and control their thoughts and feelings. In sum, our intentional, effortful activities have a powerful effect on how happy we are, over and above the effects of our set points and the circumstances in which we find ourselves. If an unhappy person wants to experience interest, enthusiasm, contentment, peace, and joy, he or she can make it happen by learning the habits of a happy person.*
>
> – From *The How of Happiness*

The lessons that follow offer a variety of ways to begin your happiness practice. You don't have to make all of them part of your practice, although you could! Pick one, two, or three and experiment with them. Make a conscious effort to practice happiness by doing those things every day.

LIVING THE LESSON

- Make a commitment to practice happiness.
- Pick one, two, or three of the lessons in this book and practice them every day. If you need to, put a reminder in your calendar or on your phone. Do it! Sometimes we need support in creating new habits. That's okay.
- Keep a journal. Notice if what you are doing is helping to increase your happiness. If it's not, experiment with another lesson.

- Be kind to yourself. Don't beat yourself up if you miss a day in your practice. Changing our behavior isn't easy—even when we really want to change.

[1:1] Sonja Lyumbomirsky, *The How of Happiness: A Scientific Approach to Getting the Life You Want* (Penguin Books, 2008).
[1:2] Shawn Achor, *The Happiness Advantage: The Seven Principles of Positive Psychology That Fuel Success and Performance at Work* (Crown Business, 2010).
[1:3] Kira Newman, "Six Ways Happiness Is Good for Your Health." *Greater Good Magazine* (July 28, 2015). https://greatergood.berkeley.edu/article/item/six_ways_happiness_is_good_for_your_health

Lesson 2

WHAT'S THE DIFFERENCE BETWEEN WELLNESS AND WELL-BEING?

Wellness is the complete integration of body, mind, and spirit—the realization that everything we do, think, feel, and believe has an effect on our state of well-being.

– GREG ANDERSON

WELLNESS

Our focus on happiness, wellness, and resilience encompasses the concept of well-being. You might be wondering what the difference is between wellness and well-being. Interestingly, there has been a fair amount of discussion in recent years about the distinction between them.

The *Merriam Webster Dictionary* defines wellness as a "quality or state of being in good health, especially as an actively sought goal." While this definition implies that wellness is not a static activity, experts in the field of wellness make clear that it is much more than a quality or state of being.

According to the Global Wellness Institute, "wellness is the active pursuit of activities, choices, and lifestyles that lead to a state of holistic health."[2:1] According to the Institute, there are two fundamental aspects to wellness:

1. Wellness is not a passive or static state but rather an "active pursuit" that is associated with intentions, choices, and actions as we work toward an optimal state of health and well-being.
2. Wellness is linked to holistic health—that is, it extends beyond physical health and incorporates many different dimensions that should work in harmony.

Wellness is more than merely physical health. Wellness is focused on our physical, social, and emotional state, as well. Wellness also encompasses the positive things we *can do* to live a healthier and happier life. According to the Global Wellness Institute, there are six dimensions to the concept of wellness:

- **Physical:** A healthy body through exercise, nutrition, sleep, etc.
- **Mental:** Engagement with the world through learning, problem-solving, creativity, etc.
- **Emotional:** Being in touch with, aware of, accepting of, and able to express one's feelings (and those of others).
- **Spiritual:** Our search for meaning and purpose in human existence.
- **Social:** Connecting with, interacting with, and contributing to other people and our communities.
- **Environmental:** A healthy physical environment free of hazards; awareness of the role we play in bettering rather than denigrating the natural environment.

Historically, the legal profession has not given much consideration to individual attorney wellness or providing an environment that supports the six dimensions of wellness listed above. In fact, the profession has encouraged a culture that is antithetical to wellness. We're sure you've heard lawyers brag about being the first one in the office and the last to leave. It has always been a badge of honor for lawyers to work ridiculously long hours. Maybe you are one of those lawyers. And if you are working remotely from home, the work is there 24/7. This is a recipe for stress, health problems, and burnout. There is an entire body of research that shows how working those long hours jeopardizes your health.

We think it is important to widen our focus beyond what individuals can do to boost their own wellness and also address the law firm culture. Law firms can create workplaces that foster wellness for all of their employees. In *Dying for a Paycheck: How Modern Management Harms Employee Health and Company Performance—and What We Can Do About It*, Jeffrey Pfeffer notes that "employers seldom consider the workplace itself and what occurs there as important causal factors affecting individual behavior."[2:2] Pfeffer, a professor in the Graduate School of Business at Stanford University, has a message that anyone responsible for running a law firm needs to hear.

> *My fundamental message is simple: employers have a choice. They can implement practices that enhance human well-being—physical and mental health—thereby reducing their own costs from employee medical expenses, absenteeism, workers' compensation insurance costs, and the productivity loss from having employees who are physically at work but not really there (a problem called presentism in the research literature). Such employer actions will also reduce the costs to society from people's poor physical and mental health and the harm done to individuals. Simply put, employers can make decisions to improve people's lives in fundamentally important ways. Or alternatively, employers can, either intentionally or through ignorance and neglect, create workplaces that literally sicken and kill people.*
>
> – From *Dying for a Paycheck*

WELL-BEING

Wellness and well-being are sometimes referred to interchangeably. But, while they share some commonalities, they are not the same. Wellness involves a lifestyle, activities, and choices that lead to a state of holistic health. There are specific things you can do to boost your wellness. Activities, choices, and lifestyles are objective. Well-being, on the other hand, is a perception—not an objective reality.

One of the best definitions we have for well-being is that it is more ephemeral than wellness. It's a feeling, a state of mind. While wellness focuses on what you can do to support holistic health, well-being is about the feelings that can be associated with that objective reality.

According to research conducted by Gallup and reported in 2021, "Wellbeing encompasses the broader holistic dimensions of a well-lived life."[2:3] *The 2017 Report of the National Task Force on Lawyer Well-Being*[2:4] defines well-being as a continuous process in which lawyers seek to thrive in each of the following areas:

- **Emotional Health:** Recognizing the importance of emotions; developing the ability to identify and manage our own emotions to support mental health, achieve goals, and inform decision-making; seeking help for mental health when needed.
- **Occupational Pursuits:** Cultivating personal satisfaction, growth, and enrichment in work; financial stability.
- **Creative or Intellectual Endeavors:** Engaging in continuous

learning and the pursuit of creative or intellectually challenging activities that foster ongoing development; monitoring cognitive wellness.

- **Spirituality or Purpose in Life:** Developing a sense of meaningfulness and purpose in all aspects of life.
- **Physical Health:** Striving for regular physical activity, proper diet and nutrition, sufficient sleep, and recovery; minimizing the use of addictive substances; seeking help for physical health when needed.
- **Social Connections:** Developing a sense of connection, belonging, and a well-developed support network while also contributing to our groups and communities.

HOW DOES WELLNESS AFFECT WELL-BEING?

While wellness and well-being may not be the same thing, they are inextricably linked. One of the positive side effects of boosting wellness is increasing your sense of well-being. Wellness, therefore, becomes an integral component of your overall well-being.

While wellness is an important part of well-being, it is only a part. For example, a person may exercise regularly and eat healthy foods. This is an important aspect of our wellness. But that same person may have few close friends and feel no sense of purpose in their life—two integral factors in well-being. We need to focus on both our wellness and well-being to feel our best and boost our overall sense of happiness. Happiness, wellness, and well-being are the three-legged stool that supports our physical, mental, and emotional health. The lessons in this book provide strategies to help you in each of these areas.

LIVING THE LESSON

- Pay attention to your own wellness. When was the last time you had a physical? Do you schedule regular visits to the dentist? Are you getting the health screenings that you need each year? If not, it is time to start taking care of YOU.
- Remember, small changes and small improvements add up over time. Most people don't have to make radical changes to their lifestyles to experience significant changes in their level of wellness.

- You can also use The Flourishing Scale—a brief, eight-item measure of your own sense of well-being. You can download The Flourishing Scale from the Greater Good Science Center here: https://ggsc.berkeley.edu/images/uploads/The_Flourishing_Scale.pdf
- Start experimenting with the lessons in this book today. Don't wait!

[2:1] Global Wellness Institute Staff, "What is wellness?" *Global Wellness Institute* (February 1, 2022). https://globalwellnessinstitute.org/what-is-wellness/

[2:2] Jeffrey Pfeffer, *Dying for a Paycheck: How Modern Management Harms Employee Health and Company Performance – and What We Can Do About It* (Harper Business, 2018).

[2:3] Ryan Pendell, "Wellness vs. Wellbeing: What's the Difference?" *Gallup* (March 22, 2021). https://www.gallup.com/workplace/340202/wellness-wellbeing-difference.aspx

[2:4] Bree Buchanan and James Coyle, "National Task Force on Lawyer Well-Being: Creating a Movement To Improve Well-Being in the Legal Profession." *American Bar Association* (August 14, 2017). https://www.americanbar.org/content/dam/aba/images/abanews/ThePathToLawyerWellBeingReportRevFINAL.pdf

ADDITIONAL RESOURCES

- *Well-Being Toolkit for Lawyers and Legal Employers*, Created by Anne M. Brafford for use by the American Bar Association.
- The Institute for Well-Being in Law: www.lawyerwellbeing.net

Lesson 3

WHY RESILIENCE MATTERS.

Resilience isn't a single skill. It's a variety of skills and coping mechanisms. To bounce back from bumps in the road, as well as failures, you should focus on emphasizing the positive.

– JEAN CHATZKY

WHAT EXACTLY IS RESILIENCE?

According to *Dictionary.com*, resilience is "the power or ability of a material to return to its original form, position, etc., after being bent, compressed, or stretched." Think of how a sponge bounces back to normal after being squeezed. The American Psychological Association defines resilience as "the process and outcome of successfully adapting to difficult or challenging life experiences, especially through mental, emotional, and behavioral flexibility and adjustment to external and internal demands." Resilience allows us to adapt when we are faced with adversity, trauma, tragedy, threats, or other significant sources of stress—whether those stressors are deadlines in a case, dealing with a difficult client, challenges in our personal relationships, or facing our own serious health problems. Research tells us that we are better than sponges. We can develop the ability to bounce back better than normal.

Resilience is very different than being numb. Resilience means you experience, you feel, you fail, you hurt. You fall. But, you keep going.

—YASMIN MOGAHED

WHAT RESILIENCE IS NOT

Resilience is not a personality trait or a quality some people are born with, and others are not. Resilience is, as Jean Chatzky notes in the quote opening this lesson, a set of skills and behaviors that we can learn and develop.

Just as we can strengthen our muscles through regular exercise, we can strengthen our resilience by understanding ourselves and making small changes each day. That sounds simple, but simple does not mean easy. The key is to focus on small changes—noticing your thoughts, how you are feeling, and experimenting with practices that have been proven to increase resilience. This may not be easy, but we can promise you, it is well worth it.

HOW YOUR BRAIN AFFECTS YOUR LEVEL OF RESILIENCE

Our neural pathways—the fabric of our brain—are not set during childhood. Our brains are constantly changing. We have the ability to affect these neural pathways throughout our life.

> *The brain is continually remodeling itself as you learn from your experiences. When you repeatedly stimulate a circuit in your brain, you strengthen it. You learn to be calmer or more compassionate the same way you learn anything else: through repeated practice.*
>
> – From *Resilient: How to Grow an Unshakable Core of Calm, Strength, and Happiness* [3:1]

STRATEGIES TO DEVELOP RESILIENCE

In their book, *Micro-Resilience: Minor Shifts for Major Boosts in Focus, Drive, and Energy*,[3:2] authors Bonnie St. John and Allen P. Haines outline five strategies they call "The Five Frameworks" that can help build resilience. Together, The Five Frameworks create micro-resilience. Micro-resilience focuses on making small shifts throughout the day to create long-lasting increases in your energy, productivity, and well-being. Let's take a look at how to apply each of these frameworks to your day.

1. Refocus Your Brain

Focus and resilience go hand-in-hand. The first step in building focus for you and your team is to change the interruption culture at your firm. Most law firms foster a culture of interruptions and distractions. In both your physical office and in virtual settings, there is a fine line between collaboration and continual interference. Continual interference is exhausting and the enemy of building resilience because constant interruptions take a toll on your personal productivity and effectiveness at work. Research tells us that living with constant interruptions impairs your ability to build resilience, as well! You can counteract this by scheduling uninterrupted work time throughout your day.

Another resilience killer is multitasking. When we try to multitask, we are not more productive—we are less productive. Our brains can only focus on one thing at a time. Sure, we can walk and chew gum at the same time, but more complex tasks require our full attention. We know we shouldn't try to text while we are driving because both tasks require our attention. So, don't text and drive, and strive to limit or eliminate multitasking.

> *It is fine to perform two or more tasks at once if quality or accuracy is not a high priority. But the widespread belief that multitasking makes us more efficient in our busy lives is far more myth than science. At every business level, from the C-suites to the front lines, we see rampant exhaustion and intellectual depreciation as a result of this misunderstood social norm.*
>
> – From *Micro-Resilience: Minor Shifts for Major Boosts in Focus, Drive, and Energy*

Try these additional strategies to refocus your brain and build your micro-resilience:

- Simplify your routines.
- Create AND USE checklists.
- Resist the urge to micromanage. When you micromanage your team, you are training them to bother you incessantly.

2. Reset Your Primitive Alarms

Understanding what pushes your buttons or sets you off is critical to developing micro-resilience. When someone pushes our buttons, our natural reaction is for our amygdala (or lizard brain) to kick into high gear. In his book *Emotional Intelligence*,[3:3] Daniel Goleman refers to this reaction as an "emotional hijacking."

People can react to an emotional hijacking in different ways. If you're paying attention, you'll know when it happens. You may get flushed. Your heart may race. Some people feel it in the pit of their stomachs. Your goal is to notice and decide how to react. In other words, don't let yourself get hijacked in the first place.

One of the most effective ways to do this is to consciously interrupt what your amygdala is trying to do to you. Begin to take deep breaths using your diaphragm or belly—not your chest.

> *Shifting from constricted breathing to relaxed, natural breathing turns off the body's fight-or-flight stress response. This balances the autonomic nervous system and produces a feeling of relaxed energy, mental clarity, and a physiological state that promotes health and vitality.*
>
> – From *The Mind Body Solution*[3:4]

Learning to breathe from your diaphragm takes practice, but you can start by placing your hand on your abdomen and imagining that with each breath, you are trying to inflate a balloon in your belly. Relax and begin to notice the rise and fall of your belly—not your chest—when you breathe.

3. Reframe Your Attitude

Our brains are hardwired to pay more attention to negative stimuli than positive ones. This propensity is referred to by scientists as a negativity bias. Our negativity bias essentially causes us to interpret all uncertainty as a threat. When our ancestors saw the leaves of a bush rustle, they instinctively thought, *Run! It's a tiger!* It may not have been a tiger, but if it was, they either outran it or became dinner. And while the negativity bias has helped us evolve over the millennia, it does not serve us well in the 21st Century. In fact, research is clear that it is time for us to develop a positivity bias.

Developing a positive attitude is essential to developing your resilience. It may sound cliché, but life is not as much about what happens to us but how we react to what happens to us. We explore this idea further in *Lesson 10: Don't Be So Judgy,* and *Lesson 19: Identify Your Invisible Saber-Toothed Tigers.*

> *Positive emotions flood our brains with dopamine and serotonin, chemicals that not only make us feel good but dial up the learning centers of our brains to higher levels. They help us organize new information, keep that information in the brain longer, and retrieve it faster later on. And they enable us to make and sustain more neural connections, which allows us to think more quickly and creatively, become more skilled at complex analysis and problem solving, and see and invent new ways of doing things.*
>
> – From *The Happiness Advantage: The Seven Principles of Positive Psychology That Fuel Success and Performance at Work*[3:5]

Decades of research across a variety of fields have also linked positivity to everything from earning more to greater longevity, improved health, and better relationships. Turns out, having a positive attitude also affects how resilient we are.

There are a number of ways that you can begin to cultivate positivity in your life. One of the most powerful is to keep a gratitude journal in a notebook, on your phone, or tablet. Each night before you go to sleep, write down three things that you are grateful for. This exercise asks you to look back on your day and notice the good things in your life. It also helps you to begin noticing things to be grateful for throughout the day. But don't just write down three things—feel the emotion—*feel grateful*. This is what triggers positivity in your brain—the feeling, not the writing. We know this might be challenging to some but try it. Experiment with it.

4. Refresh Your Body

In *The Other 90%,*[3:6] author and neuroscientist Robert Cooper suggests taking what he refers to as "strategic pauses" and "essential breaks" as a means to boost energy and mental clarity. Now, we know that these pauses and breaks not only boost your energy and mental clarity, but also build resilience. Cooper suggests that the following components be part of any strategic pause or essential break:

- **Deepen and relax your breathing.** Focus on your breathing while you take ten relaxed breaths.
- **Change your view.** Look out the window or at photos of loved ones. It's important to give your eyes a break from staring at the computer screen throughout the day.
- **Sip ice water.** The refreshing cold stimulates energy production and raises alertness. Research has also found that sipping ice water can help burn calories throughout the day.
- **Get up and move!** Every time you get up and move or stretch, you receive an energy boost and achieve increased mental clarity. Keep a few free weights in your office so that when you take breaks, you can get in a few reps!
- **Add some humor or inspiration.** Stop for a moment to recall a fond memory or watch a funny video on YouTube. You'll inject positivity into your day, which helps boost your creative thinking.

A strategic pause is no more than 30 seconds that's taken every 30 minutes throughout the day. Each pause gives you the opportunity to breathe and stretch. An essential break is just a bit longer, two to three minutes, that's taken about every 90 minutes. Essential breaks are tied to what scientists refer to as our ultradian rhythms or ultradian cycles. About every 90 to 120 minutes throughout the day, our bodies move from periods of higher alertness to lower alertness. Giving ourselves breaks as we move through these cycles refreshes our mind and body.

Nutrition is another important component of refreshing your body. Be mindful of what you put in your body. Eat foods that energize you and make you feel good. There are some universals with respect to nutrition: limit your intake of sugar; watch your carbohydrates; look for good protein snacks; don't drink too much caffeine; etc. You need to know your body. What foods create a sense of optimal health and well-being for you?

5. Renew Your Spirit

In *Micro-Resilience*, the authors talk about renewing your spirit as analogous to discovering your purpose. They specifically note that this framework must "be approached differently" from the other frameworks in the book. In order to renew your spirit throughout the day, you must first know your purpose. For more information on this, see *Lesson 5: Get Clear on Your Why.*

Discovering your purpose is essential to not only building your level of resilience but also to your overall level of happiness. Discovering your purpose can be a lifetime pursuit. Unfortunately, neither law school nor the legal profession places much importance on discovering your purpose. As Steven Keeva noted in his book, *Transforming Practices: Finding Joy and Satisfaction in the Legal Life,*[3:7] "Caring, compassion, a sense of something greater than the case at hand, a transcendent purpose that gives meaning to your work—these are the legal culture's glaring omissions." Decades later, Keeva's quote from 1999 still resonates.

While finding a "transcendent purpose" may be one of the legal culture's glaring omissions, it does not need to be one of yours. Discover your purpose and know your purpose so that you can work each day to renew your spirit and build resilience.

Once you know your purpose, that purpose will impact every aspect of your practice and your life. If you are true to your purpose, it will impact the clients you choose to work with, the matters you take on, the team who surrounds you, and even how you decide to market your practice. The very act of living and working in concert with your purpose will energize you and offer you countless opportunities throughout the day to renew your spirit.

USING MICRO-RESILENCE TO BUILD MACRO-RESILENCE

Perhaps Friedrich Nietzsche said it best—or maybe it was Kelly Clarkson, "That which does not kill us makes us stronger." The Five Frameworks outlined in *Micro-Resilience* provide a wonderful starting point to build resilience. But they are only a starting point. These micro habits support broader habits, like getting the right amount of exercise, nutrition, sleep, and other components of a healthy and happy life.

LIVING THE LESSON

- Experiment with The Five Frameworks throughout your day.
- Take small steps! Start by focusing on just one framework until it becomes part of your routine—just like brushing your teeth in the morning.
- While The Five Frameworks are not necessarily presented in order of importance, we'd suggest starting with the first one on the list—Refocus Your Brain. When you can begin to do this, you can do anything.
- Wherever you start. Just start. And be kind to yourself along the way.

[3:1] Rick Hanson and Forrest Hanson, *Resilient: How to Grow an Unshakable Core of Calm, Strength, and Happiness* (Harmony Books, 2018).
[3:2] Bonnie St. John and Allen Haines, *Micro-Resilience: Minor Shifts for Major Boosts in Focus, Drive, and Energy* (Center Street, 2017).
[3:3] Daniel Goleman, *Emotional Intelligence* (Bantam Books, 2006).
[3:4] Jeffrey Rossman, T*he Mind Body Solution: The Breakthrough Drug-Free Program for Lasting Relief from Depression* (Rodale Books, 2010).
[3:5] Shawn Achor, *The Happiness Advantage: The Seven Principles of Positive Psychology That Fuel Success and Performance at Work* (Crown Business, 2010).
[3:6] Robert Cooper, *The Other 90% - How to Unlock Your Vast Untapped Potential for Leadership and Life* (Crown Business, 2002).
[3:7] Steven Keeva, *Transforming Practices: Finding Joy and Satisfaction in the Legal Life* (American Bar Association, 1999).

ADDITIONAL RESOURCES

- Greater Good Science Center: https://greatergood.berkeley.edu/
- Anxiety & Depression Association of America: https://adaa.org/

Lesson 4

BEAT BURNOUT.

If you feel burnout setting in, if you feel demoralized or exhausted, it is best, for the sake of everyone, to withdraw and restore yourself.

– *Dalai Lama*

The term *burnout* was coined in the 1970s by psychologist Herbert Freudenberger when he attempted to make sense of his own perplexing symptoms and struggled to identify an existing pathology that properly encompassed it. Left without anything to draw from in the world of medicine, he borrowed *burnout* from the field of engineering, where it literally meant "to burn until fuel is exhausted." While initially conceptualized as a means of understanding his own experience through his work, Freudenberger discovered that it was (and is still today) a common and problematic experience in the helping professions. And, yes, you as a lawyer, are in a helping profession.

A BRIEF HISTORY OF BURNOUT

Over the past 40 years, the definition of burnout has evolved to be understood as a form of chronic mental strain that develops over time in response to prolonged periods of high stress. Working from this definition, we see that burnout is our stress leveling-up. It is the result of our brains being in a constant state of fight-or-flight for so long that our very baseline of functioning changes. It's important to understand that while stress is an inherent and necessary part of the human condition, burnout is a problematic state, and the two are different.

ACUTE STRESS VERSUS CHRONIC STRESS

Acute stress (i.e., normal stress) occurs in short bursts, such as when we are giving a presentation or struggling to meet a deadline. Chronic stress happens when these acute stress events are prolonged or when we are subject to ongoing psychological demands, such as a consistently stressful academic or professional environment. These require many hours of work with little room for error or relaxation. Anything, in particular, come to mind? It's chronic stress that results in burnout.

When experiencing acute stress, our cortisol and adrenaline levels increase along with our blood pressure, breathing rate, heart rate, and muscle tension. Our bodies are wired to recover from occasional acute stress by regulating cortisol and adrenaline production, and returning to pre-acute stress levels shortly after a moment of stress.

Chronic stress results in a different course of events. When we experience chronic stress for prolonged periods, our fight-or-flight response and recovery systems are so overworked that our bodies struggle to produce cortisol, resulting in adrenal fatigue. The chronic stress resulting from overwork, or even just the constant thinking about work, drains the body of its energy reserves, redirecting them to the primary muscles groups to maintain the consistent state of fight-or-flight. This leads to symptoms such as dizziness, tiredness, headaches, sweating, and shortness of breath. It can also lead to anxiety, panic attacks, depression, a disruption of your hormonal system, and hormonal imbalances.

YOUR BRAIN ON BURNOUT

The impacts go beyond the externally observable changes. Burnout also has a physical impact on the brain. Research has confirmed that a brain in a constant state of burnout experiences premature aging of the amygdala, the anterior cingulate cortex, and the medial prefrontal cortex, all areas that regulate our stress response. Moreover, the distribution of resources in our brains shifts to make up for this depletion, leaving other parts of our brains in a less-than-optimal state or even impaired. This is especially critical for lawyers, as our work primarily relies on skills controlled by the prefrontal cortex, an area of the brain that experiences significant depletion throughout the course of a stress response. When operating under chronic stress or a state of burnout, we are working with impaired brains.

BURNOUT SIGNS AND SYMPTOMS

PHYSICAL	EMOTIONAL	COGNITIVE

• Difficulty Sleeping
• Changes in Appetite
• Otherwise Unexplained Pain:
  • Headache
  • Neck Pain
  • Muscle Tension
• Dizziness
• Shortness of Breath
	• Irritability
	• Excessive Worry
	• Apathy
	• Intrusive Negative Thoughts (often related to hopelessness and worthlessness)
		• Difficulty Concentrating
		• Increased Procrastination
		• Disorganization
		• Indecisiveness
		• Forgetfulness

BURNOUT SIGNS AND SYMPTOMS IN LAWYERS

PHYSICAL	EMOTIONAL	COGNITIVE
• Inability to relax at bedtime • Night waking due to work-related worries • Work-related nightmares • Emotional eating while working • Emotional eating to avoid work • Working in lieu of eating • Headaches, muscle tension, difficulty breathing, and neck pain	• Emotional outbursts with colleagues and family • Excessive work-related worry • Apathy about work-related results • Intrusive negative thoughts related to whether one is worthy of one's salary, title, accolades, etc. • Lack of interest in previously enjoyed activities	• Difficulty concentrating • Work rushed just before deadline • Lengthy "To Do" list • Disorganization of files and desk • Fear and delay in case strategy • Difficulty determining priorities • Missed deadlines • Unanswered mail, emails, and voicemails

ETHICAL IMPLICATIONS OF BURNOUT ON THE LEGAL PROFESSION

Burnout's ability to impair brain function means that a burned out brain is more likely to make mistakes than a healthy brain. If your brain is burned out, you are more likely to make mistakes that can create serious consequences for your client, your employer, and you. Just some of the problematic behaviors connected to lawyer burnout with potential ethical consequences include missed deadlines, sub-par work product, lack of communication with clients and colleagues, and a failure to advocate for your client's interests.

The high stakes of trying to function in a state of burnout mean that we need to be intentional in how we address it. We may not be able to change the state of the world or of our legal profession, but we can work to change what we, as individuals, do for ourselves.

LIVING THE LESSON

- Look back at how your stress levels have cycled in past years. There is often a pattern that emerges that we can use to anticipate when we are more likely to experience burnout. Once we see the patterns, we can strategically take things off our plates (e.g., unnecessary activities, tasks, obligations) and intentionally incorporate practices that refuel us, such as social connection, routines, and mild to moderate exercise.
- Keep a log of when and why you feel stressed and upset. Look for a pattern of what tends to trigger negative thinking and emotions in you.
- Using the data you collected from your stress cycles and your thought/feeling tracking, identify opportunities to strategically plan your day, your week, your quarter, and your year with the intention of mitigating the intensity.

Lesson 5

GET CLEAR ON YOUR WHY.

It is not enough to be busy; so are the ants.
The question is: What are we busy about?

– *Henry David Thoreau*

On the surface, Henry David Thoreau may appear to be talking about the quality of our activities. Analyzed further, we understand that he is referring to what drives the actions that keep us busy. In short, he is referring to our values. Values are our *why.*

VALUES FROM A PSYCHOLOGICAL PERSPECTIVE

The Invisible Hand

The word *value* is commonly used to mean beliefs. From the perspective of psychology, values are internal drives that guide our choices. These are not judgments of righteousness or external power, but rather internal cognitive constructs that reflect how we identify meaning and priorities for ourselves. Until intentionally examined, values are usually nonconscious forces that fuel our behaviors, thoughts, and emotions.

The Unattainable Finish Line

The word *value* is also commonly and mistakenly used interchangeably with a goal. Whereas goals can be accomplished, values cannot. Using a classic analogy, running a marathon is a goal, whereas fitness is a value. You can achieve running a marathon, but fitness requires constant work without a finish line. Your *why* is a constant choice.

The Perceived Paradox

Values as both passive internal forces and active pursuits may at first seem like a paradox. However, these two views are phases of how values play a role in our lives. As the invisible hand, values unconsciously drive our thoughts, behaviors, and emotions. After intentional examination, values become reasons for the choices we make.

THE SCIENCE BEHIND HOW VALUES MATTER TO LAWYER WELL-BEING

Understanding our values matters. Not because values define a *good* person, but rather your values empower you to make intentional and authentic choices. These choices, whether they be about time, money, career, relationships, etc., can predict and sustain lawyer well-being and satisfaction.

In a 2015 study, Professor Lawrence Krieger and Dr. Kennon Sheldon examined why lawyers were so unhappy in their work.[5:1] Their study was at first deemed a failure due to the lack of statistically relevant data, pointing the researchers in one direction or another. There were just too many reasons for lawyers to be unhappy in their careers. That's right. We know it's sad, but it's also not surprising.

Initially disappointed but not dissuaded from gaining a deeper understanding of lawyer happiness and satisfaction, Krieger and Sheldon did not give up. They continued the study by revisiting the data. With fresh eyes, they investigated what, if anything, could make lawyers grinding away in the legal profession genuinely satisfied with their work. Although they initially set out to study *why* lawyers were so unhappy, instead they found predictors of lawyer happiness and satisfaction.

The data revealed three predictors of lawyer happiness and satisfaction:

1. Authenticity
2. Interconnectedness
3. Competence/Internal Motivation

WHAT IS AUTHENTICITY FOR LAWYERS?

Authenticity is a measure of the disparity between our values and our behaviors. It's a measure of how closely our actions reflect our *why*. Krieger and Sheldon found that the smaller the disparity between a lawyer's values and behaviors, the higher the measured happiness and satisfaction: the greater the disparity, the lower the measured happiness and satisfaction. For example, a lawyer whose top values include independence and freedom is more likely to be happier as a solo practitioner or independent contractor rather than an associate or partner in a big law firm. A lawyer who highly values order may find it easier to access and experience a sense of well-being in a transactional niche as opposed to litigation.

Krieger and Sheldon's data is consistent with prior research on self-determination theory and clinical models such as acceptance commitment therapy. Both disciplines have also found that an alignment between values and behaviors is key to well-being.

VALUES IN PRACTICE

The Values Inventory is an exercise that asks you to identify your top five-to-seven values and how or whether, they manifest in your behaviors. It can be a useful tool because it puts into black and white what your top values are and where you can intentionally choose behaviors that align with them. For many, this is easier said than done because it can be difficult to choose between the values. It's easy to get lost in the intangible nature of values. This is by design. The exercise requires us to think through what truly matters to us in living our lives.

While you may encounter difficulty in narrowing the number down to five or seven, you may also find it difficult to determine whether a value is *valid* or not. To be clear, all values are *valid.* There is no moral judgment regarding any value; kindness is neither better nor worse than confrontation. This is not about being a *good* or *bad* person. It's about knowing and committing to the *why* behind what keeps us busy every day. Finally, try to exercise some patience and self-compassion as you go through the exercise. It can be tough, tougher than it looks, for many people.

The ultimate source of a happy life is the attention we pay to our inner values.

– *Dalai Lama*

LIVING THE LESSON

- Conduct your own Values Inventory:
    - Select your top five-to-seven values from a values list such as the one below or from a list found through a simple Google search.
    - As you wrap up each day (weekend included), set a timer for five minutes, take out your list and write a sentence or two about a behavior you engaged in that involved each value. Keep it short

and simple. No need to overachieve here. Note that not each value will be lived out each day, and it's possible that some values aren't being lived out at all. Do this for two weeks (or more if you are in a groove).

- At the end of two weeks, survey your results. How are your values aligning with your behaviors?
- Where you see strong alignment, keep it up and explore further.
- Where you observe a gap, think back to the missed opportunities you had to live out those values. How can you choose those more values-aligned options next time?

[5:1] Lawrence Krieger, "What Makes Lawyers Lawyers Happy? A Data-Driven Prescription to Redefine Professional Success." 83 Geo. Wash. L. Rev. 554 (2015). https://ir.law.fsu.edu/articles/94/

LIST OF VALUES		
• Abundance	• Fairness	• Order
• Acceptance	• Faith	• Passion
• Achievement	• Family	• Peace
• Authenticity	• Fitness	• Perseverance
• Balance	• Freedom	• Quality
• Bravery	• Friendship	• Respect for Others
• Care for Others	• Fun	• Responsibility
• Commitment	• Generosity	• Security
• Competence	• Gratitude	• Self-Respect
• Contention	• Harmony	• Self-Control
• Cooperation	• Honesty	• Serenity
• Courage	• Humor	• Service to Others
• Creativity	• Independence	• Simplicity
• Dependability	• Innovation	• Spirituality
• Discipline	• Joy	• Stability
• Diversity	• Kindness	• Success
• Effectiveness	• Knowledge	• Teamwork
• Empathy	• Love	• Well-being
• Equality	• Loyalty	• Winning
• Excellence	• Openness	• Wisdom

Lesson 6

SET AN INTENTION FOR YOUR DAY.

Work on purpose. Play on purpose. Rest on purpose.
Do not let yourself or anyone else waste your time.

– *Izzy Victoria Odiase*

What is the first thing you do when you wake up every morning? What is the very first thing you do the moment you open your eyes? Do you know? Maybe, when you open your eyes, your brain is already racing—thinking about all the work that needs to be done—the deadlines that are looming, or the call to the crabby client that you have to make. Or, maybe you're thinking about what you need to do for your kids, your parents, or your pets.

We have all felt that feeling of stress immediately upon waking in the morning. Sometimes, the stress of our lives can be overwhelming. But it doesn't have to be. There is a better way.

Years ago, Louise Hay, an author credited with being one of the founders of the self-help movement, recorded an audiobook entitled *101 Power Thoughts.*[6:1] It was first released as a set of CDs! Remember those? Now, *101 Power Thoughts* is available at audible.com. One of the power thoughts that Louise suggests is to set an intention for your day. There is power in creating intentional focus for your life each and every day. Setting an intention for your day is not the same as a goal. Think of it more as a focus.

Of course, how we spend our days is how we spend our lives.

– *Annie Dillard*

The reality of our world has led many of us through days that are unfocused—and lives that are unfocused. We constantly feel that we are being pulled in a million different directions. We often feel that we are too busy. But are we busy with the right things?

> *Many of the lies we have been told since birth crowd out the things in life that matter most. Instead of enjoying the benefit of calm, intentional living, we hurry from one needless triviality to another. And in the end, nobody wins. Don't get so busy chasing the wrong things that you miss enjoying the right things.*
>
> – From *The More of Less*[6:2]

Setting an intention for your day is a powerful way to focus on the things that matter most to you. You can begin to live your life intentionally by taking small steps every day. As Ruth Bader Ginsberg once said, "Real change, enduring change, happens one step at a time." What is true for society is true for each one of us in both our personal and professional lives.

HOW TO SET AN INTENTION FOR YOUR DAY

Your intention can be a simple sentence like this one: Today, I will commit myself to ________________.

Here are some examples:

- Today, I will commit myself to eat healthy.
- Today, I will commit myself to exercise for 30 minutes.
- Today, I will commit myself to be the best parent I can be.
- Today, I will commit myself to appreciate the people who work
- with me.
- Today, I will commit myself to really listening to what my clients need.

HOW TO CHOOSE YOUR INTENTION

On his website, becomingminimalist.com,[6:3] Joshua Becker provides five questions to help you choose your intention for the day.

- What are the two or three most important things you want to accomplish in your life? Does one stand out above the others?
- Is there a role in your life you feel compelled to succeed at?
- Is there an overarching spiritual belief or worldview that helps you

make sense of the world? Does it motivate you to live a full life?
- What current healthy life change are you pursuing?
- When you close your eyes at night, which daily pursuit or accomplishment leaves you feeling the most fulfilled?

While Becker suggests very broad, even lifelong intentions, an intention for the day can be just that—an intention for the day. Perhaps you have an important client meeting scheduled for the afternoon. Your intention for the day could be: *Today, I will commit myself to work toward the best outcome in the meeting with my client by truly understanding their needs.*

Finally, setting an intention for your day doesn't mean you won't sometimes be distracted and lose your focus, but it can serve as a reminder to help keep you on track. And while your intention helps you focus, it's not all you will focus on for the day. It's not a substitute for your goals and the things you will *do* during the day; your intention informs how you will focus on those goals. And remember, your intention may change from time to time—or even day-to-day, and that's okay.

LIVING THE LESSON

- Start each day by setting an intention.
- Do this before you even get out of bed. Give yourself a few quiet moments in the morning. Quiet your thoughts. Focus on the day ahead—still new and unfolding.
- What will you commit to today? What would you like this day to look like? What would you like to happen today?
- Say it out loud.

[6:1]Louise Hay, *101 Power Thoughts* (Hay House Audio, 1994).
[6:2] Joshua Becker, *The More of Less: Finding the Life You Want Under Everything You Own* (WaterBrook Press, 2016).
[6:3] Joshua Becker, "The One Sentence You Need Each Day to Set Your Intention." *Becoming Minimalist* (September 23, 2019). https://www.becomingminimalist.com/intention-setting/

ADDITIONAL RESOURCES

- Kelsey Patel, *Burning Bright: Rituals, Reiki & Self-Care to Heal Burnout, Anxiety & Stress* (Harmony, 2020).

Lesson 7

START YOUR DAY WITH A GOOD STRETCH AND SOME ENDORPHINS.

The hallmark of successful people is that they are always stretching themselves to learn new things.

– Carol S. Dweck

Stretching ourselves both physically and mentally is the only way we can grow and improve. And, while stretching ourselves beyond our comfort zone can be uncomfortable, stretching your body first thing in the morning feels good! It not only feels good, but it's also good for you. You may already stretch in the morning before you even get out of bed. Have you ever thought about why you do this? The answer is simple. Because it feels good. There is science behind those good feelings, which explains the many benefits of a morning stretch that will stay with you throughout the day.

Even though we know that stretching feels good, and we may even be aware of some of its benefits, many of us don't make stretching an intentional part of our day. If you're one of those people, you may want to rethink your morning routine.

WHY IS STRETCHING IN THE MORNING IMPORTANT?

A number of things happen in our bodies when we are sleeping. Our muscles and organs tend to relax. Consequently, our heart rate slows down, and our blood flow decreases. So, we may feel sluggish when we wake up in the morning. At the same time, if you've been sleeping in the same position all night or if you've not had a restful night's sleep, you may wake up with muscles that feel tight or even sore. That's why we almost instinctively stretch and yawn when we first wake up. Stretching increases blood flow and wakes up our muscles. Best of all, stretching in the morning helps prepare us for the day ahead.

WHAT ARE THE BENEFITS OF STRETCHING IN THE MORNING?

There are many documented benefits to stretching regularly. These benefits affect both our body and our brain. As with so many things in life, consistency is key, and a little goes a long way. You can begin to reap the benefits from morning stretching in as little as five to ten minutes a day.

> *Recent research shows that stretching for just five minutes a day, five days a week, can help improve your range of motion. A ten-minute routine is the perfect length to seriously improve your flexibility and make a wide variety of activities more enjoyable.*
>
> – From *10-Minute Stretching: Simple Exercises to Build Flexibility into Your Daily Routine*[7:1]

Below are some of the many benefits that you'll get from adding stretching to your morning routine.

- **Stretching releases endorphins and relieves stress.** Endorphins are a morphine-like substance produced by our bodies that give us feelings of joy and overall well-being. They help us tolerate pain and manage stress. Some studies have shown that endorphins can even alleviate symptoms of depression. Like most types of physical activity, stretching first thing in the morning can increase the production of endorphins.
- **Gets the blood flowing to your brain.** According to the American Council on Exercise,[7:2] stretching in the morning increases blood flow to all parts of your body—including your brain. Increased blood flow to your brain in the morning enhances focus and concentration throughout the day.
- **Improves posture and increases mobility and flexibility.** If you sit (or stand) in front of a computer for most of the day, your posture is likely suffering. And that can put a strain on not only your back but also your muscles and even your organs. By stretching each morning, you're relaxing, strengthening, and lengthening your

muscles and increasing blood flow to your organs. Another negative effect of sitting—or even standing—for long periods of time is decreased mobility and flexibility. As we get older, our mobility and flexibility tend to decrease. The less we move and stretch, the greater (and more rapid) the decrease. Stretching in the morning can help reverse this trend.

- **Enhances coordination and balance.** The more sedentary we are, the more we tend to lose coordination and balance. Both of these qualities are important as they help us react quickly to situations around us and help us lessen the likelihood of injuries.
- **Reduces pain and risk of injury.** Morning aches and pains can occur because of increased fluid in your joints and spinal discs that has accumulated overnight. Gentle morning stretches can help alleviate joint discomfort. Discomfort in your lower back can also be lessened by gentle stretching. Stretching increases the production of the synovial fluid between our joints, which helps keep us limber. As we get older and less flexible, the likelihood of injury can increase. When we are stiff, it becomes easier to injure ourselves by doing everyday tasks, like twisting to get in (or out of) the car, reaching for something on a shelf, walking up the stairs, or bending to pick up something. But according to Harvard Health,[7:3] "It's never too late to slow or even reverse the loss of flexibility."

WHENEVER YOU STRETCH, STRETCH SAFELY

There are many benefits from stretching first thing in the morning. But stretching at just about any time during the day provides similar benefits. The danger is that if you don't make it a habit—part of your routine—to stretch first thing in the morning, you're more likely to forget to stretch later in the day. Finally, while many common stretches are considered safe for most people, they may not be safe for every individual. Be sure to talk with your doctor or health care professional about the stretches that are best for you.

LIVING THE LESSON

- Incorporate five-to-ten minutes of stretching into your morning routine.

- Do this as soon as you get out of bed when your muscles are warm and relaxed.
- Find stretches that work for you. The book *10-Minute Stretching* by Hilery Hutchinson is a great place to start.
- Be patient with yourself.

[7:1] Hilery Hutchinson, *10-Minute Stretching: Simple Exercises to Build Flexibility into Your Daily Routine* (Rockridge Press, 2021).

[7:2] www.acefitness.org

[7:3] Harvard Health Publishing, "A Flexible Way to Stretch." *Harvard* (May 1, 2019). https://www.health.harvard.edu/staying-healthy/a-flexible-way-to-stretch

Lesson 8

THE ONE THING THAT CAN CHANGE EVERYTHING.

All things change when we do.

– David Whyte

The lawyers we work with come to us because they want to change something about their practice or their life. Some want to manage their time more effectively. Some want more income. Some want more control over their practice. Some want to rediscover what they "used to love to do." And just about everybody wants less stress in their life. There is an intrinsic feeling that life could be better, more fulfilling. Something just doesn't feel right. Something needs to change.

Here is the good news: change is possible. And here is the challenge: change is challenging, and it starts with you. If you don't change, nothing in your world will change. It is such a simple concept. But as we often say to our clients, simple doesn't mean easy.

WHAT IS THE ONE THING THAT CAN CHANGE EVERYTHING?

Meditation. If you're thinking that meditation means sitting cross-legged on the floor or that it is some type of religious practice, let that idea go. While you can meditate sitting cross-legged on the floor, and your meditation practice can involve religion or spirituality, those things don't need to be part of a meditation practice. Think of meditation as training—or retraining—your brain. That training brings with it a whole universe of benefits to both your emotional and physical well-being.

SOME BENEFITS OF MEDITATION

The benefits of meditation are myriad. Meditation can help you manage stress. It can help you limit distractions, increase your focus, and boost your productivity. Meditation can also help you boost your positivity, happiness, and feelings of well-being. According to the Mayo Clinic, meditation helps us to clear away the "information overload" that accumulates each day and negatively impacts our emotional well-being. Additional benefits of meditation include the following:

- Increasing Self-Awareness
- Reducing Negative Emotions
- Increasing Creativity
- Increasing Patience and Tolerance
- Gaining New Perspectives

Research also suggests that meditation can help with physical conditions, such as chronic pain, heart disease, high blood pressure, sleep issues, and anxiety.

THROUGH MEDITATION, YOU CAN USE YOUR MIND TO CHANGE YOUR BRAIN

Meditation can literally change your life. How? Through meditation, you can use your mind to change the neural pathways in your brain, breaking life-long patterns of thinking and behavior. The neural pathways in our brains are not set during our childhood, as scientists believed during most of the 20th Century. Rather, our brains are dynamic and capable of creating new neural pathways throughout our lives.

Neuroscience has discovered that our brains are constantly changing. Neuroplasticity is the term scientists use to express this concept. And the most exciting aspect of what we have learned about neuroplasticity is that *we can affect these pathways*. We can even create new pathways. Through meditation, we can use our mind to change our brain.

ONE FINAL THOUGHT ON THOUGHTS

If practicing meditation seems intimidating because you think that meditation is about stopping thoughts, let that thought go. Meditation is not about stopping thoughts. In fact, as Kelly McGonigal points out in her book,

The Willpower Instinct,[8:1] "Being bad at meditation is good for self-control." Why? A wandering mind is perfectly normal during mediation. The more you notice your mind wandering during meditation and bring it back to what you were focusing on, the more likely you will notice when your mind is wandering during the rest of the day.

As Jeena Cho notes in her book, *The Anxious Lawyer,*[8:2] "Meditation is not about getting rid of all your thoughts; it's learning not to get so lost in them that you forget what your goal is. Don't worry if your focus isn't perfect when meditating. Just practice coming back to the breath, again and again."

Meditation gives us a new perspective on how to interact with our own thoughts. As we do this, we begin to see choices that we may have never seen before.

> *Whatever our particular mental patterns, eventually, we begin to see they are patterns, not the result of a reasoning process or a choice. As we are able to see more and more of our thoughts as just reflexive thinking, we realize we don't necessarily have to believe them. By taking our thoughts less seriously, we give ourselves more power to choose what to believe, rather than simply being at the mercy of whatever might pop into our minds at any given time. This shift in how we interact with our own thought processes can have surprisingly broad-reaching consequences, giving us much more freedom of action in personal and professional settings.*
>
> – From *The Anxious Lawyer: An 8-Week Guide to a Happier, Saner Law Practice Using Meditation*

GETTING STARTED

There are many excellent resources on mediation available. Below are three resources to get you started.

Meditations to Change Your Brain: Rewire Your Neural Pathways to Transform Your Life, by Rick Hanson, a neuropsychologist, and Rick Mendius, a board-certified neurologist. This book is only available as an audiobook, as it contains numerous guided meditations. The audiobook provides fascinating scientific research on how our brains work and what we can do to affect how our brains grow and change.

The Anxious Lawyer: An 8-Week Guide to a Happier, Saner Law Practice Using Meditation, by Jeena Cho and Karen Gifford. Written by lawyers, this book provides a solid foundation for starting a meditation practice. The authors explain how meditation can be used to inform your legal practice, and they give clear instruction on how to develop your practice over the eight-week program.

Headspace (iOS and Android). If you're ready to start experimenting with meditation but are not ready to commit to an eight-week program, check out the *Headspace* app. It is a great place to start experimenting with your own meditation practice. *Headspace* is constantly being updated with new meditations and classes. It offers guided meditations as short as three minutes. It is a wonderful place to start your journey.

LIVING THE LESSON

- Make a commitment to experiment with meditation.
- Don't be afraid to start small; even five minutes of meditation can make a difference.
- Remember, consistency is key. Five minutes—or even three minutes—of meditation each day is better than thirty minutes once a week.
- Be patient and kind with yourself. If you miss a day, that's okay. You're starting a new practice, a new habit. Research tells us it can take up to six attempts to start a new behavior before it sticks. Know that missing a day is just part of the process. Tomorrow is another day. You can do this.

[8:1] Kelly McGonigal, *The Willpower Instinct: How Self-Control Works, Why It Matters, and What You Can Do To Get More of It* (Avery Trade, 2013).

[8:2] Jeena Cho and Karen Gifford, *The Anxious Lawyer: An 8-Week Guide to a Happier, Saner Law Practice Using Meditation* (American Bar Association, 2016).

Lesson 9

GIVE UP ON MOTIVATION.

Show up, show up, show up, and after a while the muse shows up, too.

– *Isabel Allende*

Motivation is one of those words that take up a lot of space in well-being, productivity, and achievement culture. Thousands of books, articles, podcasts, and even YouTube videos tell us how to get and stay motivated. It's a thriving industry which has us believing that we need motivation to accomplish anything. Well, we call BS. And science agrees.

THE MYTH OF MOTIVATION

The myth about our need for motivation is marketing at its finest. Everywhere we look we are being sold something that promises to motivate us. It's understandable to want to feel motivated. Motivation feels good. It is what gets us to purchase that home gym equipment, apply to law school, and commit to numerous other things throughout our lives. Motivation is filled with promise. The feeling of motivation tempts us with the promises of deeper more meaningful feelings like calm, happiness, and pride. Feeling motivated becomes a goal in and of itself because it feels so good.

That's just it, though. Motivation is a feeling and feelings are fleeting. Feelings cannot be our primary driving force in accomplishing things. If we relied on feeling motivated to do things, then we would rarely accomplish anything, because our feelings are naturally vulnerable to a myriad of factors in our lives, both past and present. That's why so many gym memberships are purchased yet unused and so many new year's resolutions fizzle out by the end of January. Motivation may get us to the starting line, but it does not get us to the finish line. We cannot rely on a feeling to get things done.

LAWYERS AND MOTIVATION

As lawyers, the experience of working without motivation is nothing new. Did you feel like staying up late to study for the LSAT? Did you feel like losing sleep and missing out on other activities so that you could read and outline countless pages? No, of course you didn't, but you did it anyway. Why? Because something else beyond feeling motivated drove you. You may have felt motivated at certain points, but it's highly unlikely that you felt motivated all day, every day of your law school career. If you had always waited to study until you felt like it, then you probably would not be a lawyer reading this book right now.

You were able to act on something other than motivation. This is where our *why* becomes critical to our *how*. In *Lesson 5*, we discussed the importance of getting clear on your *why*. Here, we identify how you can use that *why*, not just in the big picture, but in your day-to-day. And how you can use that *why* when you feel no motivation.

EXCHANGING MOTIVATION FOR VALUES

The force that got you through law school, through the bar exam, and through the toughest times of your career so far was much more powerful than motivation. It connected you to a deeper drive, a drive defined by how you view yourself, your worth, and your role in the world.

GET CLEAR ON YOUR WHY

It's important to note that it's possible that what drives you may be a mix of healthy and unhealthy beliefs (a.k.a. values). Perhaps, they served you at some point, but no longer do. For many lawyers, but not all, those forces may have involved painful core beliefs about self-worth. If that's the case, and you now know that those beliefs are more hurtful than they are helpful to you, you can choose to let go and replace them with beliefs that are more aligned with who you are today. See *Lesson 5: Get Clear on Your Why*, for more on this. As self-aware adults, we can choose which core beliefs we keep and which ones we discard. We may have inherited our core beliefs from our families, friends, and/or culture and developed our own new ones along the way, but that doesn't mean that we must keep them.

EXPECT A CHALLENGE

Just as we need to give up on motivation, we need to accept that there will be challenges, even if we are very clear on our *why* and are aligned with the core beliefs at their foundation. Expect that discomfort, emotional or otherwise, is okay and a natural part of the human experience. This, of course, does not mean that we should aim for or accept suffering, but rather accept that discomfort is not a threat and just part of being human.

CORRECTION. IT'S NECESSARY.

Don't be afraid to revisit the fit of your endeavor. Sometimes, even if we start out connected to our deeper drive, are clear on our *why*, and are aligned with our values, things change. Perhaps the superficial circumstances evolve, or the material factors of what we work on have changed, or we have chosen to discard the core beliefs we have outgrown in favor of others. It's okay to evolve along with what works for you.

We have seen this throughout our many years of helping lawyers and across the spectrum of legal practice. Sometimes the best move is to narrow a niche or to change an area of practice. On other occasions, a shift in boundaries works well. In some cases, a change in career is the best fit. Regardless of the potential magnitude of change, if any change at all, what matters is giving yourself the opportunity to either evolve or recommit and giving up on the strive for motivation in exchange for the deeper drive that gets you there, even when you don't feel like it is key.

LIVING THE LESSON

- Get clear on your core beliefs and values. See *Lesson 5: Get Clear on Your Why*.
- Commit to action. When you do not feel motivated, but need to get something done, remind yourself of why that task matters and set a timer to work on it for twenty minutes. See *Lesson 30: Make Friends*

with a Timer. You might not finish the task in those twenty minutes, but you will have identified why the task even matters and tolerated the discomfort of the task for a short bit. See *Lesson. 19: Identify Your Invisible Saber-Toothed Tigers*. Most importantly you will have started.

- Return to that twenty-minute timer as many times as you need to.
- Once a year, revisit this lesson and make a list of what you want in your life but have not been motivated enough to pursue or maintain. Take that same list and find where those things fit into the values that you identified in the exercise in *Lesson 5*. If they don't fit into one of the values, ask, "What is the driving force behind this?" It's possible that your original reason for the pursuit no longer applies, or that you never asked what it was. Either way, knowing is critical to either finally acting on it or to making room for goals and activities that are a better fit for you in the present.

Lesson 10

DON'T BE SO JUDGY.

Be curious, not judgmental.

– *Walt Whitman*

Have you ever considered how much judging you do each day? If you haven't noticed how many times each day you judge something as good or bad, we'd like to ask you to start paying attention. You may be amazed at what you discover. We're not just taking about judging other people, which we tend to do all too frequently, whether we are consciously aware of it or not. And we're just not talking about things that happen to you.

As lawyers, we are trained to judge everything. In fact, the profession is all about judgment. But for this lesson, we'd like you to take off your lawyer hat and begin to notice all of the things you pass judgment on every, single day.

Srikumar Rao, the founder of the Rao Institute and TED speaker, is the author of *Happiness at Work.*[10:1] During a speaking engagement, he shared a significant concept from that book, which has stuck with us to this day. It's a concept we share with all of our clients.

"We go through our lives labeling everything," Dr. Rao said. "Good thing, bad thing, very bad thing." According to Dr. Rao, most of us use the *bad thing* label three to ten times more often than we use the *good thing* label. Is that true for you? It was for us. So, why does that matter?

"The moment we label something as a bad thing, that is the beginning of suffering," Dr. Rao said. This resonated with us. We began to think about our own behaviors. Hadn't there been times in our lives when we labeled something a *bad thing* in the moment, but it turned out to be a *good thing*? Of course. It may take time to see the *good thing* from the *bad thing*, but it does happen. Aren't there times in your life when something happened that you labeled a *bad thing* that turned out to be a *good thing*?

OVERCOMING OUR NEGATIVITY BIAS

Our brains are hardwired with a negativity bias. Psychology describes the negativity bias as our tendency to notice negative events more readily than we notice positive events. In addition to noticing the negative more than the positive, the negativity bias also causes us to dwell on those events and play them over and over again in our mind. We've all experienced the negativity bias. Remember that time when you received ten compliments on something and one itty-bitty criticism? Where does your mind dwell? On the compliments or the criticism? It is a biological fact that we feel the sting of criticism much more strongly that we feel the happiness or joy from praise. Think about this the next time you offer constructive criticism to your paralegal.

Negativity bias had its place in our evolution. By giving more attention to negative events which triggered our fight-or-flight response, our brains were always on high alert. Our negativity bias helped us survive and evolve over the millennia. But, while our negativity bias has helped us to survive, it's also a reason for unnecessary suffering. According to psychologist and author, Kendra Cherry, "The negativity bias can take a toll on your mental health. It can cause you to dwell on dark thoughts, hurt your relationships with loved ones, and make it difficult to maintain an optimistic outlook on life."[10:2]

There are things we can do to overcome the negativity bias, and one of the most powerful is to reframe our experiences. Resist the tug of negativity bias to label things as *bad.*

> *When you label so much of what happens to you as bad, it reinforces the feeling that you are a powerless pawn at the mercy of outside forces over which you have no control. And—this is key—labeling something a bad thing almost guarantees that you'll experience it as such.*
>
> – From *Happiness at Work*

So, do your best to resist judging experiences as *bad things.* Try to find a way to see the good, and if you can't, put a neutral label on it. "I got a flat tire," is not a *bad thing*; it's just, "a flat tire." You may never know whether that flat tire prevented you from getting in an accident five minutes later.

LIVING THE LESSON

- Pay attention to how often you judge experiences, people, and situations.
- Notice how often you label something as a *bad thing*.
- When you feel the urge to label something as a *bad thing*, pause for a moment, and ask yourself whether it's possible that it could actually be a *good thing*. If that doesn't feel possible, place a neutral label on it. A flat tire is a flat tire.
- Remember that we are all wired with a negativity bias. Think about how your words and actions may be interpreted by others and the lasting effect they may have.

[10:1] Srikumar Rao, *Happiness at Work: Be Resilient, Motivated, and Successful – No Matter What* (McGraw Hill, 2010).
[10:2] Verywell Mind, "What Is the Negativity Bias?" *Very Well Mind* (April 29, 2020). https://www.verywellmind.com/negative-bias-4589618

ADDITIONAL RESOURCES

- *Srikumar Rao. "Not a bad thing."* https://www.youtube.com/watch?v=wrd7MWZl_gI , *2 minutes, March 12, 2010.*

Lesson 11

CREATE A MINDSET OF GRATITUDE.

Enjoy the little things, for one day you may look back and realize they were the big things.

– *Robert Brault*

The idea of being grateful for the good things in life is a simple one. Regardless of what's going on in our lives, there is always something to be grateful for. While the stress in our life can sometimes make it difficult to see them, there are very good reasons to look closely for those things that make us feel grateful. Feelings of gratitude can improve everything from our brain function to wellness and our sense of well-being.

WHAT IS GRATITUDE?

At its core, gratitude is an affirmation that there are good things in the world. In *The Gratitude Project*,[11:1] the authors cite a definition of gratitude developed by Dr. Robert Emmons that explains two aspects of gratitude.

> *One is an affirmation that there are good things in the world, things from which we've benefited. Two is a recognition of where that goodness comes from—the people and things in our life that have conspired to give it to us.*
>
> – From *The Gratitude Project*

As described in *The Gratitude Project*, research on gratitude stresses the importance of relationships. Gratitude is a recognition that "we could not be who we are or where we are in life without the contributions of others." And while gratitude recognizes the importance of relationships in our lives, having a mindset of gratitude also improves the relationships in our lives. Kira M. Newman, one of the editors of *The Gratitude Project*, explains, "Gratitude is not only for the individual but also for relationships and communities. It can have ripple effects in terms of greater kindness and gratitude for everyone."

Gratitude is a way of hunting down the positive things that have happened to you, seeing them, recognizing them, and savoring them.

– Kira M. Newman

WHY GRATITUDE MATTERS

Gratitude cultivates positivity in your brain. Positivity is good for your brain because it helps you think more clearly and creatively. Barbara Fredrickson, one of the leading researchers on the effect of positive emotions on brain function, explains in her book that cultivating the emotion of gratitude is a powerful way to bring more positivity into your life.

> *The latest scientific evidence tells us that positivity doesn't simply reflect success and health. It can also produce success and health. This means that even after positivity fades, we can find traces of its impact. Beyond the present pleasant moment, your positivity has downstream consequences for the very trajectory of your life. Positivity spells the difference between whether you languish or flourish.*
>
> – From *Positivity: Groundbreaking Research Reveals How to Embrace the Hidden Strength of Positive Emotions, Overcome Negativity, and Thrive*[11:2]

When we are in a positive state of mind, our peripheral vision improves. We actually see more of the world around us. We can take in and process information more effectively. The ability to see more—literally—allows us also to see more figuratively. When we are in a positive state of mind, we can see unique solutions to problems that we might not even notice if we are in a negative state.

Scientific studies have confirmed the relationship between our physical health and mental health. As noted in *The Gratitude Project*, these studies describe how "gratitude can improve your sleep, enhance your romantic relationships, protect you from illness, motivate you to exercise, and boost your happiness." There truly is a brain-body connection. Science has shown us how feeling positive emotions can improve our health. When your brain is at its best, your body will reap the benefits.

Think of your work as a lawyer. How often do you feel positive emotions during a typical workday? The paradox is that the work lawyers do can lead to an overdose of negative emotions when the exact opposite is what your brain needs to be at its creative best. While the focus of this book is on wellness and resilience, it is also undeniable that our brains function better, and we think better when we are in a positive state of mind. That positivity benefits not only you but also everyone around you—including the clients you serve.

POSITIVITY AND GRATITUDE – A POWERFUL COMBINATION

If being positive can help our brains function more effectively and improve our well-being, how do we get more of it into our lives? Gratitude is one of the best ways to cultivate positivity. Robert Emmons, a pioneer in gratitude research at the University of California, Davis, has shown that maintaining a mindset of gratitude is not only good for you, but it can also improve your overall health, including your psychological, emotional, and physical well-being. Being grateful helps people overcome what psychologists call *negativity bias*, our tendency to dwell on problems and annoyances rather than happy or uplifting events. See *Lesson 6: Don't Be So Judgy*.

HOW KEEPING A GRATITUDE JOURNAL CAN ENHANCE YOUR WELL-BEING

Keeping a gratitude journal is a powerful way to create a mindset of gratitude. Perhaps you've heard the phrase, "You get what you focus on." Keeping a gratitude journal helps you focus on the good things in your life. That is not to say that there are no difficulties, problems, and stressors, but we can choose to focus more on the good things. We're not, for a moment, suggesting that this is necessarily an easy thing to do. And that is where journaling can be so powerful. By regularly writing down those things for which we are grateful, we can begin to create a *habit of gratitude*. According to Kira Newman:

> *Brain science has shown us that when we repeat emotions, thoughts, and behaviors, they become more automatic. They become more likely to happen in the future. Your brain can literally be changed by your behaviors and experiences. So, if you repeatedly try to think about good things that happened to you during the day or kindnesses that other people did for you, or if you try to look for the positive in a difficult situation you're having, you will train your brain to go down those paths and to have those kinds of thoughts in the future.*
>
> – FROM *THE GRATITUDE PROJECT*

No matter what the situation is . . . close your eyes
and think of all the things in your life
you could be grateful for right now.
– DEEPAK CHOPRA

ONE FINAL THOUGHT – DON'T FORCE IT

Feeling gratitude comes more easily for some people than for others. Research suggests that differences in our brain structures may make it easier for some people to feel grateful. Our genetics and personality can also influence the levels of gratitude we feel.[11:3] If you're not feeling grateful on any given day, that's okay. Your feelings are your feelings.

Forcing yourself to feel grateful can result in guilt-induced gratitude. Don't torture yourself by thoughts like, "I should feel grateful for . . ." Using the word *should* is a clue that you may be forcing yourself to feel gratitude. According to an article in Psychology Today, "A person who tries to guilt themselves into a grateful state by comparing their pain to others' may unintentionally delegitimize their feelings and worsen rather than improve their mental health."[11:4] Allow yourself to feel your feelings and acknowledge that painful feelings and feelings of gratitude aren't mutually exclusive. For example, you can feel overwhelmed and at the same time grateful for the people around you to help you through it.

Gratitude is positive, genuine, and welcoming. It should never be a source of guilt, pressure, or shame. If you're unable to feel gratitude now, try again later. No matter what you may be going through, do your best to notice and appreciate the good things in your life.

It's not that happy people are grateful, it's that grateful people are happier.
– ERIK BARKER

LIVING THE LESSON

- Cultivate a mindset of gratitude by keeping a gratitude journal. You can do this in a paper journal, on your phone, or on your tablet.
- You may want to journal every day or evening. But research has shown that journaling even once a week can enhance your mindset of gratitude.

- As you write, do your best to *feel* the emotion of gratitude. If you are writing about someone who showed you kindness during the day, recall how you felt when it happened.
- Check out thnx4.org, an online gratitude journal created by the Greater Good Science Center.
- If you're not feeling grateful, remind yourself that's okay. Feel what you feel. Your feelings matter. Don't force feelings of gratitude or beat yourself up because you *should* feel grateful.
- Be kind to yourself. Always.

[11:1] Jeremy Adam Smith et al., *The Gratitude Project: How the Science of Thankfulness Can Rewire Our Brains for Resilience, Optimism, and the Greater Good* (Oakland, CA: New Harbinger Publications, Inc, 2020).
[11:2] Barbara Fredrickson, *Positivity: Groundbreaking Research Reveals How to Embrace the Hidden Strength of Positive Emotions, Overcome Negativity, and Thrive* (Crown Archetype, 2008).
[11:3] Summer Allen, "Why Is Gratitude So Hard for Some People?" *Greater Good Magazine* (May 10, 2018).
https://greatergood.berkeley.edu/article/item/why_is_gratitude_so_hard_for_some_people
[11:4] Sarah Epstein, "It's OK Not to Feel Grateful Right Now" *Psychology Today* (March 31, 2020).
https://www.psychologytoday.com/us/blog/between-the-generations/202003/its-ok-not-feel-grateful-right-now

Lesson 12

FEED YOUR BRAIN GOOD STUFF.

Every day, stand guard at the door of your mind.

– *Jim Rohn*

Let's start this lesson with a quick experiment. First, look around you. Whether in your office, at home, or outside, look around and notice everything brown. Take just a few moments to do this, then make a mental note of all the brown things you see.

Go ahead and look around. We'll wait.

Now, close your eyes, and, when you do, make a mental list of all the things around you that are *blue.*

After we asked you to focus on looking for brown things, could you recall any blue things? You probably had some difficulty listing them, and when you opened your eyes, you might have been surprised by how much blue there is around you. This is an example of what we mean by you get what you focus on.

The experiment seems simplistic, yet it illustrates the reality of how our brains work. Our brains will seek out what they are primed to look for. If you are focused on negative thoughts, your brain will seek out more negative thoughts and experiences. So be careful what you focus on because you are likely to get more of it.

FEED YOUR BRAIN A HEALTHY DIET

Just as your body cannot serve you well if you fill it with junk food, your brain (and mind) cannot serve you well if you fill it with negativity. In *Lesson*

10, we talk about the brain's negativity bias, how it has helped us survive over the millennia, and why it no longer serves us today. There is another important aspect of the negativity bias and how it affects your health and happiness. A constant diet of negativity and stress increases the amount of the stress hormone cortisol, which causes our brain to become even more reactive and sensitive to negative experiences. By experiencing more negativity, we are literally wiring our brains to become more negative.

It's easy for us to get stuck in negative thinking and hold on to negative feelings. Think about this in your own life. For example, your law firm may get a hundred 5-star reviews on Google, then one 2-star review. Where does your brain focus? It goes directly to that 2-star review and doesn't let go. Why? Because of the negativity bias. As Rick Hanson notes in his book, *Resilient: How to Grow an Unshakable Core of Calm, Strength, and Happiness*, "In effect, our brains are like Velcro for bad experiences but Teflon for good ones."[12:1]

CURATE YOUR NEWS AND PUSH NOTIFICATIONS

If you have news apps on your phone and allow those apps to send you push notifications throughout the day, you are likely getting bombarded with negative news all day long. When was the last time you received a news-related push notification that was good news? When was the last time you received a news-related push notification that made you feel good? Think about that for a moment, then think about the cumulative effect of all that negativity on your mind and brain.

Consuming negativity throughout the day doesn't make for a healthy mental diet. And, here's the really insidious part of those push notifications, journalists and news organizations *know* that because of our negativity bias, we will pay more attention to bad news rather than good news. So, the news-related pushes will consistently be negative.

You are in charge of what you feed your brain. You can become the curator of your news. Turn off push notifications. Stop gorging on negativity. Consuming constant negativity can make us feel helpless. It can fuel more negativity and cause us to catastrophize about our situation and the world around us.

In their book, *The Power of Bad: How the Negativity Effect Rules Us and How We Can Rule It*,[12:2] authors John Tierney and Roy Baumeister share fascinating, science-based research on why curating our news sources (and our online friends) can have a powerful, positive impact on our lives and our world view.

> *We are richer, healthier, freer, and safer than our ancestors could have ever hoped to be, yet we don't enjoy our blessings. We prefer to heed—and vote for—the voices telling us the world is going to hell. Instead of seizing opportunities and expanding our horizons, we seethe at injustices and dread disasters—and all too often respond by making things worse.*
>
> – FROM *THE POWER OF BAD*

Science has shown us that we simply cannot have a healthy mind if it is filled with constant negativity. Just as we must eat healthy foods to have a healthy body, we must feed our brain good stuff to keep our minds healthy.

LIVING THE LESSON

- Understand the negativity bias.
- Turn off push notifications from news apps.
- Take control of when and how you consume news. Turn off the firehose. Don't gorge yourself on the news. There are many alternatives to the news, such as listening to music, audiobooks, and podcasts. Try something different!
- Take a news diet one day a week. This isn't easy, but you may want to experiment with it.

[12:1] Rick Hanson and Forrest Hanson, *Resilient: How to Grow an Unshakable Core of Calm, Strength, and Happiness* (Harmony Books, 2018).

[12:2] John Tierney and Roy Baumeister, *The Power of Bad: How the Negativity Effect Rules and How We Can Rule It* (Penguin Press, 2019).

Lesson 13

DAYDREAM.

Daydream, imagine, and reflect. It's the source of infinite creativity.

– Deepak Chopra

Studies show that we daydream, i.e., think about something other than the here and now, as much as 47 percent of our waking hours. Were you discouraged from daydreaming by grownups when you were little? If you were, there's a good chance that you believe daydreaming is a waste of time. You might even feel guilty when you let your mind wander during the day. If this is you, we have some good news. Daydreaming can be a healthy way to deal with stress and lessen anxiety.

While daydreaming has numerous positive aspects, it can also be detrimental if: it fosters procrastination, your daydreams focus on negative thoughts, or you ruminate about painful situations. This lesson focuses on how you can use daydreams as *positive fantasies* to reach your goals, enhance your creativity, and boost your productivity.

DAYDREAMING CAN HELP YOU REACH YOUR GOALS

Science tells us that daydreaming can bring with it a number of benefits. And, as ironic as it may seem, daydreaming may actually help us improve our focus. Gabriele Oettingen, a professor of psychology at New York University and author of *Rethinking Positive Thinking,*[13:1] reports how research suggests daydreaming can hone our focus to help us reach our goals. According to

Oettingen, "The obstacles that we think most impede us from realizing our deepest wishes can actually hasten their fulfillment." Daydreams or "positive fantasies," as Oettingen calls them, can give us direction to act.

Daydreams may give us direction, but they may not prompt us to take action. While Oettingen encourages daydreaming, she suggests a specific approach to daydreaming that she calls "mental contrasting." In a nutshell, mental contrasting says, "Go ahead and fantasize about a goal or something you want in the future. But don't stop there. As you daydream, ask yourself what is getting the way of your dream becoming a reality. Ask yourself what obstacle is stopping you from achieving your goal." According to Oettingen's research, this contrast between your current reality and future state sets your subconscious mind to work on how to overcome the obstacle.

DAYDREAMING CAN ENHANCE CREATIVITY AND PROBLEM SOLVING

Just as daydreaming can help improve focus, it can also help enhance creativity and problem-solving. According to the research described in *Creativity and the Wandering Mind*,[13:2] daydreaming can improve our creativity by allowing us to become disengaged from a problem. When we are able to disengage and let our mind wander, our unconscious memory can process information and generate new ideas and creative insights.

If you have ever had an "Aha!" moment regarding a problem you've been working on while doing something completely unrelated, you've experienced exactly what the scientists are talking about. When you let your mind wander, your mind is experiencing the *incubation effect* that is also at play when you can step away from your work and come back to it in a day or two. When you are able to do this, you'll often gain new insights and produce a better work product.

DAYDREAMING CAN BOOST PRODUCTIVITY AND PERFORMANCE

When we daydream, we drift away for a while then come back to what we were doing. These episodes of un-focusing and refocusing can boost our productivity and performance. Moreover, the feeling of being refreshed from a daydream helps us prepare for the next task. A study published in the *Journal of Business and Psychology* reported that "mind-wandering may be able to be used strategically to enhance the work experience . . . and may be used as a micro-break from work demands."[13:3] Micro-breaks during the workday help combat fatigue and stress while boosting resilience. See *Lesson 3: Why Resilience Matters*.

So, if you feel guilty when you daydream, let it go! Daydreaming gives us all sorts of benefits. Erin Westgate, a professor of psychology at the University of Florida, refers to daydreaming as the ability to think for pleasure. She asserts that it is "part of our cognitive toolkit that's underdeveloped. It's something that sets us apart. It defines our humanity. It allows us to imagine new realities."[13:4]

Scientists are continually making discoveries about how our brains work. Their research into the benefits of daydreaming shows that having our "head in the clouds" may be a benefit to us right here on earth.

LIVING THE LESSON

- Daydream with purpose. Experiment with mental contrasting during your daydreams. Identify obstacles to your wishes and dreams and let your subconscious mind work on overcoming them.
- Is there a complex problem you're working on? Are you stuck? Schedule intentional daydreaming time. You may come up with the perfect solution.
- Set a deadline three days before a project is due. Finish the project by your self-imposed deadline and set the work aside for a couple of days. Come back to it with insights informed by the incubation effect.

[13:1] Gabriele Oettingen, *Rethinking Positive Thinking: Inside the New Science of Motivation* (Penguin Group, 2014).
[13:2] David Preiss, Diego Cosmelli and James Kaufman, *Creativity and the Wandering Mind: Spontaneous and Controlled Cognition* (Academic Press, 2020).
[13:3] Kelsey Merlo et al., "A qualitative study of daydreaming episodes at work." *Journal of Business and Psychology* 35, (2020): 203–222. https://doi.org/10.1007/s10869-018-9611-4
[13:4] Interview with Erin Westgate, "Why we're so bad at daydreaming, and how to fix it." *University of Florida News* (March 4, 2021). https://news.ufl.edu/2021/03/daydreaming/

Lesson 14

SURROUND YOURSELF WITH THINGS YOU LOVE.

Whatever you put around yourself, you will be the mirror of it. Surround yourself with things you love.

– *Marcel Wanders*

How many hours do you spend in your office each day? Whether you work in a brick-and-mortar law firm or from a home office, you probably spend at least eight hours a day in your office. You might even spend some of your weekends there, too. If you're spending that much time in your office, it should be a place where you are surrounded by things you love—things that make you smile and feel happy when you see them. The more we can do to consciously create happiness in our environment, the more happiness we will feel. That may seem deceptively simple, yet it's true.

When you think about surrounding yourself with things you love, think as broadly as possible. Your office environment has many facets of color, decor, organization, ergonomics—even aroma (scent can have a powerful effect on your mood and sense of well-being). While possessions and tangible items don't bring lasting happiness, they can be powerful touchstones and reminders of happiness. What are your touchstones?

Make your physical surroundings as beautiful as possible.

– *Alexandra Stoddard*

Make your office yours. Make it a place you enjoy. You'll feel better about it, and as a result, you'll be more productive and effective. In *Joy at Work: Organizing Your Professional Life,*[14:1] Marie Kondo and co-author Scott Sonenshein provide a step-by-step process for tidying up and organizing your professional space. You may have heard of Kondo from her book, *Spark Joy*, or her popular Netflix series. You may have also heard her tag-line question, "Does it spark joy?" Kondo's advice: "If it doesn't spark joy, get rid of it." Our advice: "Surround yourself with things you love." There's a pretty good chance the things you love will spark joy, too.

We realize you're not going to love everything in your office. Some things are primarily functional, like your office chair and the monitors and keyboard on your desk. But if you think about it, shouldn't those things make you feel happy and joyful? Your chair should be comfortable and support you, and make you feel wonderful. Your monitors should be aesthetically pleasing. Your keyboard should be clean, in working order (no broken or sticky keys!), and ergonomic.

In addition to things like photos and mementos that spur happy memories, consider those things that pull you toward a happy future: reminders of the trip you are planning to take; the home renovations you may be planning; the masterclass or retreat you're looking forward to. Whatever those things are, keep them front and center so they can help to boost happy feelings throughout the day.

And while you're looking for ways you can bring more of what you love into your office surroundings, get organized! Clutter has a powerful, negative effect on our psyche. For the vast majority of us, clutter does not contribute to our happiness, well-being, or resilience. See *Lesson 16: Enter Through Beauty* and *Lesson 29: Get Organized.*

LIVING THE LESSON

- Take an inventory of your office. Notice what you love and what you don't.
- Wherever possible, get rid of those things in your office environment that you don't love.
- Replace functional items that are worn out or just don't work for you anymore.
- Add things to your office that you love and make you feel happy. Be scrupulous in your choices.
- Repeat these steps from time to time. Don't keep things you don't love in your office just because they've always been there.

[14:1] Marie Kondo and Scott Sonenshein, *Joy at Work: Organizing Your Professional Life* (Little, Brown Spark, 2020).

Lesson 15

SPEND MONEY ON EXPERIENCES, NOT THINGS.

We are the sum total of our experiences.

– *Thomas Gilovich*

Think back for a moment on some of the best gifts you've ever received. This might take you back to when you were little to a special birthday present or perhaps your first bike. Or maybe you recall something you bought for yourself—a new phone or a new car. At first, those things undoubtedly brought you happiness—even joy. But how long did that happiness last? Even now, as you think back on those things, are you thinking about the thing or how it made you feel? You probably recall the feeling more than the thing.

If you recall the feeling that thing brought you, you are most likely recalling an experience related to that thing. For example, you may be recalling the thrill of learning to ride a bike—not the bike, itself. This is because research has shown that the feelings of happiness that things provide fade much more quickly than the feelings of happiness that come from our experiences. A twenty-year study by Cornell University Professor Thomas Gilovich found that while things can make us happy for a while, we soon adapt to them, and the feelings of happiness fade.

> *One reason that people are often tempted to spend their money on material goods rather than experiences is that the here and now of experiences is so fleeting. People often say, "If I opt for the [experience], it will be over in a flash, but at least I'll always have the [possession]." The irony is that although this is true in a material sense, it is not true psychologically. A vast literature attests to people's remarkable capacity for adaptation, which robs them of the ability to appreciate things to which they are constantly exposed, like their couches, clothes, and cars.*
>
> – From "*Waiting for Merlot: Anticipatory Consumption of Experiential and Material Purchases.*"[15:1]

New things are exciting at first, but eventually, we adapt to them. On the other hand, experiences stay with us. Recalling a wonderful vacation, hike in the mountains, or concert can bring you happiness years later. That's because, according to Gilovich and other researchers, experiences become a part of us. In an interview with *Forbes*, Gilovich explained, "You can really like your material stuff. You can even think that part of your identity is connected to those things, but nonetheless, they remain separate from you. In contrast, your experiences really are part of you. We are the sum of our experiences."[15:2]

While vacations, concerts, and days at the spa can be wonderful, positive experiences, don't limit yourself to big-ticket items. Look for little opportunities to create experiences throughout your day. Lawyers get so caught up in the work—work—work mindset, we don't give ourselves enough time throughout the day to just chill out or have a good laugh. See *Lesson 20: Have a Good Laugh.*

LEARN TO TAKE IN THE GOOD AND SAVOR POSITIVE EXPERIENCES

In his book, *Resilient: How to Grow an Unshakable Core of Calm, Strength, and Happiness,*[15:3] Rick Hanson talks about the concept of "taking in the good." *Taking in the good* is all about enriching those positive experiences we have, truly feeling them, and letting them sink deeply into us. Hanson lists five ways to enrich positive experiences so that they stay with you to help create positive neural connections in your brain. Hanson notes that any of the methods listed below will help increase the impact of a positive experience. But you don't have to use all of these approaches with every experience to get the benefit of taking in the good.

1. **Lengthen it.** If it is a short experience, stay with it for five, ten, or more seconds. As Hanson says, "neurons that fire together, wire together." Whether the experience is a seemingly small one, like noticing a beautiful blue sky above you on your morning walk, or a big thing, like seeing a Broadway show or concert, capture the feeling.
2. **Intensify it.** Hansen uses the phrase "Turn up the volume." Really focus on it.
3. **Expand it.** Notice other elements or aspects of the experience. If you've had an Aha! moment or discovery while researching a case, notice how you are feeling. Revel in it!

4. **Freshen it.** Our brains love the new and novel. We are wired to notice those things. Do your best to notice what's interesting or different about an experience. As Hanson says, "Imagine that you are having the experience for the very first time."
5. **Value it.** Hanson notes that we learn from what is relevant to us, personally. Everyone is different. Notice why the experience is important to you, why it matters to you, and how it could help you.

LIVING THE LESSON

- Look for opportunities—no matter how small—to create happy experiences.
- Practice *taking in the good* as often as you can. Pay attention when you have a positive experience.
- Pay attention to even fleeting moments, like noticing a blue sky above you or a few minutes spent throwing a ball with your dog, which can help to build your reserve of happy experiences.

[15:1] Amit Kumar, Matthew Killingsworth, and Thomas Gilovich, "Waiting for Merlot: Anticipatory Consumption of Experiential and Material Purchases." *Psychological* Science vol. 25 issue 10 (2014): 1924 – 1931. https://doi.org/10.1177/0956797614546556

[15:2] Travis Bradberry, "Why You Should Spend Your Money on Experiences, Not Things." *Forbes* (August 9, 2016). https://www.forbes.com/sites/travisbradberry/2016/08/09/why-you-should-spend-your-money-on-experiences-not-things/?sh=55205c436520

[15:3] Rick Hanson and Forrest Hanson, *Resilient: How to Grow an Unshakable Core of Calm, Strength, and Happiness* (Harmony Books, 2018).

Lesson 16

ENTER THROUGH BEAUTY.

Cluttered closets mean a cluttered mind.

– Louise Hay

The phrase "Enter through beauty" is from the audiobook *101 Power Thoughts,* a collection of positive affirmations by Louise Hay.[16:1] One of the *power thoughts* she shares in her book is, "My home is a peaceful haven." She talks about how you can feel love in a house by putting love into every room. She says that when you come home, you should enter through beauty.

The simplicity of this phrase, "Enter through beauty," is a wonderful reminder of how important our surroundings are to us and how they can impact our happiness. It's a fact that our surroundings can affect everything from our mood to our performance and creativity. While there are things in our environment that we may not be able to change, there are some things we can.

In an article published at verywellmind.com,[16:2] April Snow, a Licensed Marriage and Family Therapist (LMFT), writes about how aesthetics are one of the most potent environmental factors impacting our mental health. According to Snow, "Cluttered spaces can create feelings of overwhelm and anxiety, while tidy spaces can invoke a sense of calm. To help with this, have colors and objects in your environment that are meaningful, which can boost mood." In other words, you'll likely be happier if you surround yourself with beauty.

What is the first thing you experience when you arrive home? If you enter your house through your garage, your garage is the first thing you experience.

When the garage door goes up, do you smile to yourself and think, "Ah... I'm home," or do you see an enormous mess that nags at you? Does it make you think of all the projects you want to complete? If it's the latter, do something about it. See *Lesson 28: Stop Tolerating Your Tolerations.*

You don't have to do it all at once. Start small. Hang some art on the walls or photos that make you smile. Things that are beautiful to you. Make sure that the first thing you see when you pull into your garage is something that makes you feel good and happy to be home.

LIVING THE LESSON

- Get rid of the junk. Remember, your trash may be someone else's treasure. Give away what you no longer want or need.
- If you have a garage, keep it clean and tidy. If you want to clean it up and the project seems overwhelming, break it down into small steps, or hire someone to help you or do it for you.
- Hang a piece of art or pictures on the wall that make you smile and feel happy when you arrive home.
- Give yourself a deadline. Commit to completing the project in the next two weeks or whatever timeframe works for you.

[16:1] Louise Hay, *101 Power Thoughts* (Hay House, 2004).
[16:2] Sara Lindberg, "How Does Your Environment Affect Your Mental Health?" *Very Well Mind* (Updated January 25, 2021). https://www.verywellmind.com/how-your-environment-affects-your-mental-health-5093687

Lesson 17

GET ENOUGH SLEEP.

The amount of sleep required by the average person is five minutes more.

– *Wilson Mizner*

Do you get enough sleep? If you're like most people, you probably don't. Most of us love a good snooze alarm. Our brains need about eight hours of sleep each night to be at our best. Yet getting those eight hours is not easy. It often feels like there is just one more thing to do before bedtime. As a result, we are a sleep-deprived culture.

In a 2013 study conducted by Gallup, researchers found that 40 percent of Americans got fewer than seven hours of sleep each night. And 43 percent reported that they would feel better with more sleep.[17:1] Perhaps unsurprisingly, Gallup's research showed that the number of hours we sleep has decreased in recent decades. Gallup didn't single out lawyers in its research, but we'd bet that law is among the most sleep-deprived professions in the country. Lawyers live in a culture that for decades has said, "Work long, work late, no matter what you're working on."

Although the amount of sleep someone needs to be at their best varies, the National Sleep Foundation recommends an average of seven to nine hours per night for adults over age eighteen. Science cannot prescribe the exact amount of sleep a person needs. But what science can tell us, according to researcher and molecular biologist John Medina, is that not getting enough sleep is really bad for us. Medina is the author of *Brain Rules: 12 Principles for Surviving and Thriving at Work, Home and School.*[17:2] Medina's Brain Rule #7 is all about sleep, and the title of that chapter says it all: Sleep well, think well.

The best bridge between despair and hope is a good night's sleep.
– E. Joseph Cossman

Before we talk about why a lack of sleep is bad for us, let's take a quick look at all the good things sleep does for us. There are tremendous amounts of research demonstrating the value of a good night's sleep. Sleep boosts our wellness and capacity for learning. It supports our sense of well-being and mental health, which builds our resilience. It supports the executive function of our brain that is critical to decision-making. Sleep helps us process and organize our memories and experiences so that we can call upon them later. And sleep doesn't have to occur just during the night. Naps boost our brainpower, too. One NASA sleep study reported by Medina in *Brain Rules* showed that "a 26-minute nap improved a pilot's performance by more than 34 percent."

No day is so bad it can't be fixed with a nap.
– Carrie Snow

Getting enough sleep is also critical for the function of our immune system. In *Why We Sleep: Unlocking the Power of Sleep and Dreams,*[17:3] researcher Mathew Walker notes:

> *Sleep fights against infection and sickness by deploying all manner of weaponry within your immune arsenal, cladding you with protection. When you do fall ill, the immune system actively stimulates the sleep system, demanding more bed rest to help reinforce the war effort. Reduce sleep even for a single night, and that invisible suit of immune resilience is rudely stripped from your body.*
>
> – From *Why We Sleep: Unlocking the Power of Sleep and Dreams*

Getting enough sleep produces tons of healthy benefits, not to mention you just feel better when you've had enough sleep. Unfortunately, lack of sleep—especially chronic sleep debt (the cumulative effect of not getting enough sleep)—can be disastrous for our brains. In *Brain Rules,* Medina catalogs a litany of problems caused by not getting enough sleep. One study found that certain body chemistries of a healthy thirty-year-old allowed to sleep only about four hours a night for six consecutive nights looked more like the body chemistries of a sixty-year-old. And, when they were allowed to return to their normal sleep patterns, it took them almost a week to return to their thirty-year-old systems!

Sleep is closely connected to our moods. You know this because of how you feel when you don't get enough sleep. Inadequate sleep can increase stress and irritability. Numerous studies have shown that a chronic lack of sleep can increase our risk for anxiety and depression. In fact, poor sleep—either too much or too little—is one of the most common symptoms of depression.

> *The bottom line is that sleep loss means mind loss. Sleep loss cripples thinking in just about every way you can measure thinking. Sleep loss hurts attention, executive function, immediate memory, working memory, mood, quantitative skills, logical reasoning ability, general math knowledge. Eventually, sleep loss affects manual dexterity, including fine motor control—and even gross motor movements, such as the ability to walk on a treadmill.*
>
> – From *Brain Rules: 12 Principles for Surviving and Thriving at Work, Home, and School*

So, if you want to be a happier, healthier, more resilient lawyer, do your best to get enough sleep.

Finish each day before you begin the next, and interpose a solid wall of sleep between the two.

– Ralph Waldo Emerson

LIVING THE LESSON

- If you're not sure how much sleep is the right amount for you, keep a journal and note how much sleep you've had when you feel your best.
- Create good sleep habits.
- Turn off electronics—phones, tablets, and computers—at least 30 minutes before sleeping.
- Keep your bedroom dark. Even the light from electronic clocks can disturb your sleep. Turn them over or shield the light.
- Keep your bedroom cool. Sleep research says that we sleep better when we're just slightly cool. Many sleep experts suggest a temperature around 65°F to 70°F for sleeping. Find out what is comfortable for you.

Visit the National Sleep Foundation (www.sleepfoundation.org) for more information on how to get a good night's sleep.

[17:1] Jeffrey Jones, "In U.S., 40% Get Less Than Recommended Amount of Sleep." *Gallup* (December 19, 2013). http://www.gallup.com/poll/166553/less-recommended-amount-sleep.aspx
[17:2] John Medina, *Brain Rules: 12 Principles for Surviving and Thriving at Work, Home and School* (Pear Press, 2008).
[17:3] Mathew Walker, *Why We Sleep: Unlocking the Power of Sleep and Dreams* (Scribner, 2017).

ADDITIONAL RESOURCES

- Sleep Medicine at Harvard Medical School, "Sleep and Mood." Harvard (December 15, 2008). http://healthysleep.med.harvard.edu/need-sleep/whats-in-it-for-you/mood

Lesson 18

SMILE MORE.

Sometimes your joy is the source of your smile, but sometimes your smile can be the source of your joy.

– Thich Nhat Hanh

Law is a serious business. Lawyers spend most of their time looking for potential problems, spotting issues, and envisioning worst-case scenarios. As a lawyer, you not only have to deal with thorny issues that arise in your cases but also thorny clients, annoying opposing counsel, and prickly judges. These things can definitely make smiling throughout the day seem almost ridiculous. But you might have a good reason to smile and not even know it. Smiling can make you happier.

The theory that our behavior can influence our emotions has been debated among psychologists for over a hundred years. In 1872, Charles Darwin first expressed the idea of, "The free expression by outward signs of an emotion intensifies it."[18:1] In 1884, William James went even further, writing that if a person does not express an emotion, he has not felt it at all.[18:2] Over the years, psychologists have debated, at times debunked, and at other times found evidence supporting the idea that smiling can help enhance the emotion of happiness. Interestingly, research does support the theory that frowning can reinforce unpleasant feelings, like pain or emotions of fear and disgust.

Scientists have no clear answer as to why our facial expressions influence our emotions, as they seem to. In *The How of Happiness*, author Sonja Lyubomirsky shares the findings from numerous psychological studies that suggest "Simply taking on the facial expressions and postures of happiness can go a long way to make you experience joy."[18:3] It seems acting like a happy person can make you feel happier. According to Lyubormirsky, "pretending that you're happy—smiling, engaged, mimicking energy and enthusiasm—not only can earn you some of the benefits of happiness (returned smiles, strengthened friendships, successes at work and school) but can actually make you happier."

Guy Kawasaki, author of *Enchantment: The Art of Changing Hearts, Minds, and Actions*,[18:4] wrote about the importance of smiling as part of creating likability in a business context. His advice? Make crow's feet. By that, he means to engage your whole face and your eyes when you smile. Think pleasant thoughts. It is true that first impressions matter. Smile for yourself and those around you. It might change your whole perspective.

Appearances matter—and remember to smile.

– Nelson Mandela

LIVING THE LESSON

- Try this experiment to see if Thich Nhat Hanh's quote at the beginning of this lesson is true for you—that your smile can be the source of your joy.
- Every time you look in the mirror, smile at yourself.
- Really smile. Make crow's feet. Do your best to *feel* happiness and joy.
- Notice how you feel.
- Do you feel happier? If your answer is yes, then keep smiling.

[18:1] Charles Darwin, *The Expression of the Emotions in Man and Animals* (London: John Murray, 1872).
[18:2] William James, "What Is an Emotion?" *Mind*, 9(34) (1884): 188-205. http://www.jstor.org/stable/2246769.
[18:3] Sonja Lyubomirsky, *The How of Happiness: A Scientific Approach to Getting the Life You Want* (Penguin Books, 2008).
[18:4] Guy Kawasaki, *Enchantment: The Art of Changing Hearts, Minds, and Actions* (New York: Portfolio/Penguin, 2011).

Lesson 19

IDENTIFY YOUR INVISIBLE SABER-TOOTHED TIGERS.

Anxiety is a thin stream of fear trickling through the mind. If encouraged, it cuts a channel into which all other thoughts are drained.

– *Robert Albert Bloch*

Stress gets a bad rap. We often treat it as if it's something to eliminate, failing to recognize that it has been responsible for our very survival as a species. The key to dealing with our stress is not to avoid it, but rather to understand it.

WE ARE EVOLUTIONARILY WIRED FOR STRESS

When we encounter a stressor, our limbic system kicks into gear. The limbic system is a group of brain structures that work together, bridging the gap between our psychological and physiological experiences. For example, when we encounter a stressor, our limbic system prepares to handle it by releasing hormones that raise blood pressure, increase heart rate, improve blood flow to the muscles and organs, and elevate breathing rate. These are the cornerstones of a fight-or-flight response. This perception of a stressor followed by a physical response designed to survive was critical to our ancestors' survival. It maximized the likelihood of surviving threats posed by enemy attacks and predators such as saber-toothed tigers.

HOW OUR ANCIENT BRAINS WORK TODAY

For most of us, our ancestors' stressors were quite different from what we, as lawyers, encounter today. While they would occasionally encounter an enemy or saber-toothed tiger intent on hurting them, modern-day lawyers encounter deadlines, doubts, fears, and (insert your unique blend of stressor here) every single day.

We may not be able to see our saber-toothed tigers (If you do, please seek professional help immediately), but they feel real, and our limbic systems do not know the difference. Whether it's a real saber-toothed tiger or an invisible one disguised as an assignment you are avoiding, the threat feels the same. While not imminently threatening to life and limb, our invisible saber-toothed tigers pose significant risks to a much more vulnerable part of ourselves—our self-worth.

THE LAWYER AND THE INVISIBLE SABER-TOOTHED TIGER

A modern-day stressor and threat to life and limb occur neurologically as one and the same. For many of the lawyers we have worked with, it makes sense that these invisible saber-toothed tigers have ranged from reading or writing an email to meeting with a difficult client, submitting a brief, arguing in court, and beyond.

It would be manageable if our limbic system had evolved to effectively deal with these threats, but it didn't. Our ancestors dealt with such levels of stress maybe a few times a week, yet we encounter them almost every day, multiple times per day. They pop up everywhere, and that takes a serious toll. We are built to survive the occasional attack, not a daily barrage.

To mitigate the negative impacts of overworking our limbic system, it's helpful to know our typical invisible saber-toothed tigers. Knowing what they are gives us an opportunity to recognize their potential impact and choose behaviors that avoid, or at least decrease, the limbic system's reaction to them. This allows our brains a chance to logically differentiate between an assignment you have kept on the backburner and a rustling in the bushes behind you.

LIVING THE LESSON

- Set a timer for five minutes and make a list of the tasks you have been avoiding and the things that have elicited feelings of discomfort for you in recent memory.
- Keep that list with you for two weeks as you go about your days. Whenever you notice that you are putting something off or feel

physically or mentally uncomfortable about something, take a moment to check that list. If it's on the list, note it with a little hashmark. If it's not on the list, add it to the list.

- At the end of two weeks, you will have a sample of which triggers have an ancestral survival response in you. Now that you have something to start with, you're in a better position to identify them for what they truly are: threats that stem from your perception rather than exclusively from facts.
- Once you understand this concept, you are equipped to question your perception of the situation, especially what is not in your immediate environment driving your fear response. You are already a step ahead because you can now identify that what you fear is not necessarily fact.
- For more on what you can do about your identified saber-toothed tigers, see *Lesson 49: Accept That You Are Not a Purely Logical Being.*

Lesson 20

HAVE A GOOD LAUGH.

Laughter is the shortest distance between two people.

– *Victor Borge*

Law offices are not where you typically hear laughter ringing through the halls. That's sad. Lawyers need more laughter. Laughter is good for us. It's also good for the people who work with us and for us. We need to reconsider infusing more laughter and happiness into our workplaces. After all, when we are feeling positive and upbeat, we are more creative and better at problem-solving. See *Lesson 11: Create a Mindset of Gratitude*. Not only that—our positivity is contagious. We have the ability to infect other people with positivity and help them to be more creative and better at problem-solving. See *Lesson 21: Make Someone Happy*.

Think about some of the people you know. Do you know people who you just love to be around? Have you known people whose very presence just makes you feel good? When you have those feelings, you are experiencing the contagion of emotions. There are a lot of good reasons to spread that contagion.

HEALTH BENEFITS OF LAUGHTER

Whether you're laughing at home, watching your favorite show, or laughing at a YouTube video during a micro-resilience break at the office, your laughter relieves stress and adds up to better health. But don't take our word for it. According to the Mayo Clinic,[20:1] there are both short-term and long-term health benefits to a good laugh. Laughter can indeed be the best medicine.

Short-Term Benefits

- Laughter stimulates organ function by increasing your intake of oxygen-rich air. It also increases endorphins released by your brain.
- A good laugh can calm you down and decrease heart rate and blood pressure.
- Laughter can also increase circulation and enhance muscle relaxation.

Long-Term Benefits

- Laughter has been shown to improve our immune system over time by decreasing stress hormones in the body. According to the Mayo Clinic, "positive thoughts can actually release neuropeptides that help fight stress and potentially more serious illness."
- Laughing can help ease pain. When we laugh, our bodies produce natural painkillers.
- Because of the release of calming hormones and chemicals, a good laugh can help you cope with difficult situations.
- And last but certainly not least, a good laugh can help improve your mood.

Laughter is one of the best stress relievers around. But here's the challenge—what's funny to one person can be not-so-funny to someone else. Where does that leave us if we want to create more happiness and positivity in the office?

"We don't laugh because we're happy, we are happy because we laugh."
– *William James*

Authors of *The Humor Code*,[20:2] Peter McGraw and Joel Warner, describe their book as a "mash-up of science and comedy." It is a seriously fun read. The book provides some broad recommendations that you can use if you want to bring more humor, laughter, and positivity into your office and your life. Below are just a few:

- It's not whether you're funny or not; it's what kind of funny you are. Be honest and authentic.

- If you can't be "ha-ha" funny, at least be "Aha!" funny. Cleverness is sometimes good enough.
- Don't be afraid to chuckle at yourself. It signals everything is okay and lets others laugh, too.
- Good comedy is a conspiracy. Create an in-group with those you want to get the joke.
- Context matters. No one will laugh if they don't know what you're talking about.
- Comedy signals an escape from the world. Create a safe, playful space where folks are free to laugh.

While sharing laughter is a wonderful way to engage with the people at work, sometimes you just need a good laugh all by yourself. Thankfully, there are lots of ways to kickstart a giggle or guffaw.

Before you criticize someone, you should walk a mile in their shoes. That way, when you criticize them, you are a mile away from them, and you have their shoes.

—*Jack Handey*

Where were we? Oh yeah . . . ways you can kickstart some chuckles.

- Take a few minutes and watch a funny YouTube video.
- Listen to a funny podcast.
- Can you bring your dog to work? We know many lawyers with dog-friendly offices. Pups not only bring smiles to you and your team, but they can also be a comfort to your clients.
- Keep photos or other items in your workspace that make you smile, laugh, or bring back happy memories.
- Spend time with people who make you laugh. It's contagious.

Whatever you do, remember this sage advice from the authors of *The Humor Code*: "The best comedy turns the world upside down. Make fun of yourself before others get a chance to do so."

Laugh as much as possible, always laugh. It's the sweetest thing one can do for oneself and one's fellow human beings.

– *Maya Angelou*

LIVING THE LESSON

- Try an experiment to see if laughing—like smiling—can make a difference in how you feel.
- Pull the corners of your mouth into a smile and give a little chuckle. Go on . . . try it.
- Notice how you're feeling—even if your laughter feels a bit forced.
- Are you a little bit less stressed? Do you feel more relaxed?
- Now, take five minutes and watch a laugh-out-loud funny video.
- Repeat this experiment every single day.

[20:1] Mayo Clinic Staff, "Stress relief from laughter? It's no joke." *Mayo Clinic* (April 5, 2019). https://www.mayoclinic.org/healthy-lifestyle/stress-management/in-depth/stress-relief/art-20044456
[20:2] Peter McGraw and Joel Warner, *The Humor Code: A Global Search for What Makes Things Funny* (Simon & Schuster, 2014).

Lesson 21

MAKE SOMEONE HAPPY.

Make someone happy
Make just one, someone happy
And you will be happy too.

– *From the song "Make Someone Happy"*
by Jule Styne, Betty Comden, and Adolph Green

Have you ever started laughing just because you heard someone else laughing? Have your eyes filled with tears at the sight of another person crying? Have you ever yawned in response to seeing a tired friend yawn? If you answered "Yes," to any of these questions, you've experienced the contagion of our moods. There are scientific reasons for our moods being contagious. Knowing this, we can make conscious choices about how we choose to infect others with our moods.

THE CONTAGIOUSNESS OF MOODS

How do you feel when you walk through the front door of your office? Are you thinking, "How can I answer that question? Every time is different. It depends on where I'm coming from—literally and figuratively." While that may be true, it's your responsibility to be aware of your mood every time you walk into your office.

Whatever your mood and attitude may be, it affects every person in your office. If you're in a good mood, everyone around you picks up on it. Contagious good moods can boost morale and productivity. Bad moods are contagious, too, and can infect everyone in the office, causing morale and productivity to plummet.

In *Primal Leadership: Unleashing the Power of Emotional Intelligence,*[21:1] authors Daniel Goleman, Richard Boyatzis, and Annie McKee explain how the leader's mood creates either a productive (resonant) or toxic (dissonant) work environment. It all starts with our limbic system and something scientists call "the open loop."

> *Scientists describe the open loop as "interpersonal limbic regulation," whereby one person transmits signals that can alter hormone levels, cardiovascular function, sleep rhythms, and even immune function inside the body of another. That's how couples who are in love are able to trigger in one another's brains surges of oxytocin, which creates a pleasant, affectionate feeling. But in all aspects of social life, not just love relationships, our physiologies intermingle, our emotions automatically shifting into the register of the person we're with. The open-loop design of the limbic system means that other people can change our very physiology – and so our emotions.*
>
> – FROM *PRIMAL LEADERSHIP*

People around you can pick up on your mood and will mirror that mood. When you are positive, warm, and upbeat, you send out emotions that create good vibes in others and a resonant climate in your office. You can feel the energy and enthusiasm of a resonant climate. It's a place where people enjoy working; where they are engaged and feel valued; and consequently, are happier and more productive.

When you are negative, cold, and irritable, you send out emotions that create a dissonant climate. We've all been in a dissonant working climate at some point in our lives. No one enjoys working in one. We know what it feels like, and it doesn't feel good. A dissonant climate is one filled with tension, discord, and toxicity. People don't want to be there, and as a result, they are much less productive than those who work in a resonant climate—and for a resonant leader.

Now, we're not saying that a resonant climate means there are never any problems or tensions in an office. There will always be pressures and deadlines in any law office. A certain level of stress can be a good thing. But prolonged, unrelenting stress and negativity diminishes our brain's capacity to process information, which dramatically reduces our productivity. According to *Primal Leadership*, "A good laugh or an upbeat mood, on the other hand, more often enhances the neural abilities crucial for doing good work."

Be nice. It is so underrated.

– THERESA JEAN-PIERRE COY, FOUNDER OF JEAN-PIERRE COY, P.A.

To be both effective and *happier*, you've got to get good at controlling your emotions and attitudes. Here's the good news: You can make a conscious decision to change your attitude at any time. It's your job to model the attitudes and behaviors you want to encourage in your team. Before you step into your next meeting or walk through the door of your office, check your attitude. Are you relaxed, or are you stressed out? Are you tight-lipped because you're still irritated by that last phone call with opposing counsel, or are you ready to smile—genuinely smile? If you're angry, frustrated, or just in a bad mood, pause for a moment as you reach for the door. At that moment, you can choose to change your attitude. We are not saying that it's easy to do, but we are saying that you must get in the habit of doing it. Otherwise, you will always be at the mercy of your own emotions rather than being in control of them.

POSITIVITY IN YOUR PRACTICE

You know the old saying, "Law school teaches you to think like a lawyer." We've never met an attorney who has said, "You know, I was so cynical and pessimistic before I became a lawyer, but law school sure changed all that!" While the critical thinking skills that law school teaches are invaluable to your role as an advocate, they can create challenges for you in other aspects of your life—especially your level of happiness. Although law school may have tried to beat it out of you, you have the ability to think critically about a situation without being cynical or negative. Lawyers must check their "lawyerly" thinking at the door. Developing this habit is essential to your happiness, health, and well-being.

Now consider the climate in your office. Is it positive or negative? Whatever the climate, environment, or mood, it is a reflection of YOU. You are being watched all the time, and your mood is highly contagious. You set the tone for your office, so make a conscious choice to set a resonant tone, not a dissonant one.

The longer I live, the more I realize the impact of attitude on life. Attitude, to me, is more important than facts. It is more important than the past, than education, than money, than circumstances, than failures, than successes, than what other people think or say or do. It is more important than appearance, giftedness or skill. It will make or break a company…a church…a home. The remarkable thing is we have a choice every day regarding the attitude we will embrace for that day. We cannot change our past...we cannot change the fact that people will act in a certain way. We cannot change the inevitable. The only thing we can do is play on the one string we have, and that is our attitude. I am convinced that life is 10% what happens to me and 90% of how I react to it. And so, it is with you...we are in charge of our attitudes.

– *Charles Swindoll*

LIVING THE LESSON

- Begin to notice your moods.
- Check your attitude—not just at the door—but throughout the day. Are you sending out upbeat, positive emotions and creating a resonant climate? Or are you sending out negative emotions that create a dissonant climate?
- Train your brain to be more positive. You may think this is impossible, but it's not. You can use *mindfulness* to literally grow your brain's capacity for upbeat, optimistic feelings. See *Lesson 8: The One Thing That Can Change Everything.*

[21:1] Daniel Goleman, Richard Boyatzis, and Annie McKee, *Primal Leadership: Unleashing the Power of Emotional Intelligence* (Harvard Business Review Press, 2013).

Lesson 22

HAVE A GOOD CRY.

I always like crying in the rain, so no one can see me crying.

– Charlie Chaplin

Crying is inherent to being human. It's a non-verbal language and our very first vocal expression upon birth. Many researchers believe that it's not just inherent but a unique trait that sets us apart from other species and evolved as a means of communication. An experience that connects all humans across cultures and time, having a good cry is an essential element of self-care.

WHAT IS CRYING?

Our eyes naturally produce three types of tears: reflex, continuous, and emotional tears. Reflex and continuous tears are 98 percent water and keep your eyes healthy and safe from debris. Emotional tears, what we refer to when we talk about having a good cry, have a different chemical composition. They contain hormones such as prolactin, serotonin, cortisol, and adrenaline. These uniquely human tears result from the limbic system, the part of the brain responsible for our fight-or-flight response and a myriad of emotions. The presence of hormones and a connection to the emotional arousal center of our brains suggests a relationship between the act of crying and a restorative process taking place within the body.

THE BENEFITS OF CRYING

- **Crying can improve your mood and is a healthy means of self-soothing.**
  We often associate crying with a worsening mood, so it can be odd to think of crying as a way to calm oneself and reduce stress. Studies have found that crying is preceded by increased activity in the parasympathetic nervous system, the system primarily responsible for resting, digestion, and getting you into a relaxed state.[22:1] It functions as a healthy self-soothing mechanism because it releases relaxation and bonding hormones, such as oxytocin and endorphins, that aid in relieving both physical and emotional pain.
- **Crying can restore your emotional equilibrium.**
  Emotional crying can happen as a response to happiness, just as it can be a response to sadness or fear. Our bodies constantly work toward maintaining equilibrium, including emotional equilibrium. Researchers at Yale University suspect that crying emotional tears helps our bodies recover from strong emotions, whether that emotion is happy or sad.[22:2]

THE DANGERS OF NOT CRYING

Crying is like sneezing in that it is a means for our bodies to release potentially harmful substances. Just like when we hold back a sneeze, when we repress the need to cry, we deny our bodies an important safety valve. As a result, we keep difficult feelings and stress hormones inside and end up engaging in what psychologists call *repressive coping*. Studies have revealed significant associations between repressive coping and cardiovascular disease, hypertension, anxiety, depression, cancer, and a less resilient immune system.

WHEN TEARS ARE A PROBLEM

While extolling all the benefits of crying, we would be remiss not to address when crying can signal a problem. Crying every day is not necessarily worrisome because some people naturally cry more than others. The concern from too much crying arises when frequent or daily crying is accompanied by sustained feelings of anxiety or depression, mainly when it affects your daily activities and becomes uncontrollable. These signs indicate a need for further evaluation and potential treatment from a healthcare professional. Regardless of the reason, it's important to allow yourself to cry.

LIVING THE LESSON

- Identify a space where it feels safe to cry. This is often by yourself in a comforting environment like your home. For others, it can be in the driveway while sitting in the car.
- If you feel like crying but can't, try watching a funny or sad movie. This can trigger your body to want to reset your emotional equilibrium through crying.
- Just let it go. Be raw. Be you. Remember that by allowing yourself to cry, you allow your body to do what it needs to take care of itself. Crying is self-care.

[22:1] Asmir Grăcanin, Lauren Bylsma, and J. J. M. Vingerhoets, "Is crying a self-soothing behavior?" *Frontiers in Psychology*, 5, Article 502 (May 2014). https://doi.org/10.3389/fpsyg.2014.00502
[22:2] Oriana Aragón, Margaret Clark, Rebecca L Dyer, and John Bargh, "Dimorphous expressions of positive emotion: displays of both care and aggression in response to cute stimuli." *Psychological Sciences*, 26(3): 259 – 73, (January, 2015). https://journals.sagepub.com/doi/10.1177/0956797614561044

Lesson 23

ADOPT A DOG OR CAT.

Petting, scratching, and cuddling a dog could be as soothing to the mind and heart as deep meditation and almost as good for the soul as prayer.

– DEAN KOONTZ

Are you a dog or cat person? We all have our particular attractions to one or the other. It turns out, though, that with respect to our health and well-being, it doesn't matter. Being in the company of furry friends of either variety is good for us on many levels.

If you already have a dog or cat in your life, you know what we're talking about. Just being around our furry children can boost our happiness—even if they've chewed a shoe or shredded every roll of toilet paper in the house. They make us feel good, but that's not all. Having a pet provides us with all sorts of benefits to our physical, emotional, and social well-being.

According to research reported by Jeremy Barron, Medical Director of the Beacham Center for Geriatric Medicine at Johns Hopkins, "Owning a pet provides an amazing array of health benefits."[23:1] Below are just some of the benefits you'll reap from your furry kid.

REDUCED STRESS

Science has proven what we've known for a long time—petting a dog or cat reduces our stress. It can calm us down and soothe our souls. Animals make us feel better, and there is a scientific reason why.

> *Scientists have also observed that interacting with animals increases levels of the hormone oxytocin. Oxytocin has a number of important effects on the body. It slows a person's heart rate and breathing, reduces blood pressure, and inhibits the production of stress hormones. All of these changes help create a sense of calm and comfort.*
>
> – From *"Why Do Pets Make Us Feel Better?"*[23:2]

Oxytocin is known as the feel-good hormone because of its ability to promote trust, empathy, and bonding in relationships. When our bodies produce more oxytocin, we feel better all over.

LOWERED BLOOD PRESSURE

Another benefit we get from our pets is lower blood pressure. According to Barron, "Petting and holding an animal allows you to enjoy the beauty of nature. It's relaxing and transcendental." When we're interacting with our pets, our breathing slows down and our heart rate slows. Both are effective in supporting lowered blood pressure.

INCREASED EXERCISE

Okay, so this one applies mostly to dog owners. Although, we've seen more than one cat taking a neighborhood walk on a leash. Mutts get us up and off our butts. Studies reported at Livehappy.com found that people who walked their dogs exercised 30 minutes more per week than non-dog owners.[23:3] And you're likely to walk faster when you hit the road with your pup.

BOOSTED IMMUNE SYSTEM

Studies have shown that petting a dog or cat can increase our levels of infection-fighting antibodies. A study from the University of Wisconsin School of Medicine and Public Health reported in Livehappy.com found that a child "at risk of developing respiratory allergies or asthma was less likely to have symptoms like eczema and wheezing if the child had lived in a house with a dog since early infancy." Get your kid that puppy! You'll both benefit.

BETTER HEART HEALTH

According to research reported by the American Heart Association, "Dog owners are 31 percent less likely to die from a heart attack or stroke than non-dog owners, and people with prior heart events who had a dog living at home had a 65 percent reduced risk of death."[23:4]

BETTER MENTAL AND EMOTIONAL HEALTH

Our pets give us unconditional love. Some researchers (and dog and cat owners) argue that they demonstrate empathy when we're going through tough times. No questions. No judgment. Just love, support, and comfort. One study found that pets actually provided more social support than humans in easing loneliness and depression.

If you're lucky enough to have a dog or cat, you already know what research has proven: our lives are better on so many levels when we have a furry member of the family. Our pets give purpose to our lives. They make us smile. They give us unconditional love. They help us live healthier, happier lives. They are furry, fuzzy bundles of joy.

If you don't have a pet or feel you're not ready—or can't—adopt one, you can still reap some of the benefits of their companionship. You can offer to walk a friend's dog or cat-sit for a neighbor. You can even volunteer at an animal shelter. But be careful. Being around all that adorable cuteness may be irresistible.

LIVING THE LESSON

- Do you already have a dog or cat? Then next chance you get—maybe right now—go and give them some love. Hugs and kisses. Maybe a nice walk. It's good for both of you.
- If you don't have a furry kid, consider adopting.
- If you can't adopt, make time to spend with furry friends.

[23:1] Editorial Staff, "The Friend Who Keeps You Young." *Johns Hopkins Medicine* (2022). https://www.hopkinsmedicine.org/health/wellness-and-prevention/the-friend-who-keeps-you-young

[23:2] Amber Bauer, "Why Do Pets Make Us Feel Better?" *Cancer.Net Blog* (April 23, 2015). (https://www.cancer.net/blog/2015-04/why-do-pets-make-us-feel-better

[23:3] Maura Rhodes, "5 Ways Our Pets Make Us Happy." *Livehappy.com* (April 15, 2015). https://www.livehappy.com/animals/5-ways-our-pets-make-us-happy

[23:4] Editorial Staff, "16 Science-Backed Reasons Adopting a Dog Could Be Good for Your Heart." *American Heart Association* (January 31, 2020). https://www.heart.org/en/healthy-living/healthy-bond-for-life-pets/a-dog-could-be-good-for-your-heart

Lesson 24

GET HIGH—A HELPER'S HIGH, THAT IS.

If you want happiness for an hour—take a nap.
If you want happiness for a day—go fishing.
If you want happiness for a year—inherit a fortune.
If you want happiness for a lifetime—help someone else.

– CHINESE PROVERB

You know how you feel right after you do something nice for someone. Perhaps it's an extra tip for the barista or buying coffee for the person behind you at the drive-thru. Maybe it's stopping to help someone who's dropped their packages in the street or helping a pro bono client having a tough time after being evicted from their home. Helping others makes us feel good. It's a universal experience, and there is a scientific reason for it. Just as exercise can create a runner's high, giving back creates what psychologists call a "helper's high."

Helper's high is a state of euphoria created by the release of endorphins in the brain—just like a runner's high. Allan Luks coined the phrase helper's high in his book, *The Healing Power of Doing Good.*[24:1] We've all felt a helper's high at some point in our life. The sensation of a helper's high feels good in the moments after performing an act of kindness or altruism because an act of kindness—in and of itself—triggers our brain to release chemicals that make us feel good.

> *The role of endorphins in our bodies has now been linked not only with the muffling of pain but also with sensations as familiar and cheerful as the feeling of a "thrill" or as dramatic as a druglike high. Today we know that we can create such sensations within ourselves by our own activities. We can trigger such brain messages by creating circumstances that are conducive to the release of*

this naturally occurring chemical substance. Helping others seems to be one such means of stimulating endorphin release.

– From *The Healing Power of Doing Good*

There is a lot—yes, a lot—of research that demonstrates why an intentional act of kindness not only positively impacts the recipient but will also positively impact you. In fact, you're more likely to feel happier about doing something kind for someone else than you are for doing something nice for yourself.

The benefits of altruism and engaging in random acts of kindness are many. Below are just a few from ProjectHelping.org. If you want to dig deeper into the science of doing good, ProjectHelping.org provides links to numerous research studies.[24:2] Here's what we know from decades of research:

- Volunteering and sharing your time with others can improve your overall happiness and mental well-being.
- Volunteering can help boost brain function.
- People who perform acts of kindness for others are more likely to report feeling happy or an improvement in their mood than people who were merely kind to themselves.
- Volunteers report lower levels of depression and enhanced well-being.
- Performing random acts of kindness boosts the release of dopamine—the *feel-good* neurotransmitter in the brain.
- People who engage in altruistic acts are better able to sustain positive emotions and recover more quickly from negative experiences.

DOING GOOD MAKES US FEEL GOOD

When we're motivated by a true spirit of generosity, we benefit as much as those on the receiving end. Jesuit priest Anthony de Mello says it this way: "Charity is really self-interest masquerading under the form of altruism… I give myself the pleasure of pleasing others." In the same vein, the Dalai Lama playfully speaks of working to benefit others as "selfish altruism."

The childhood of the human race is far from over. We have a long way to go before most people will understand that what they do for others is just as important to their well-being as what they do for themselves.

– *William T. Powers*

In his book *Authentic Happiness: Using the New Positive Psychology to Realize Your Potential for Lasting Fulfillment,*[24:3] noted psychologist Martin Seligman explains that kindness contributes to a type of durable happiness that lasts far longer than the pleasure of the endorphin rush we get from a helper's high. According to Seligman, "The exercise of kindness is a gratification, in contrast to a pleasure. As a gratification, it calls on your strengths to rise to an occasion and meet a challenge. Kindness is not accompanied by a separable stream of positive emotions like joy; rather, it consists in total engagement and the loss of self-consciousness." Seligman's research and the research of others have also found that kindness can have a significant impact on our sense of well-being in the moment. "Doing a kindness produces the single most reliable momentary increase in well-being [for the doer] of any exercise we've tested."[24:4]

Whether it's the momentary rush of endorphins and dopamine that allows us to feel a helper's high or the more durable sense of happiness and well-being, kindness is the genesis for those feelings.

I am a big believer in—if you can't figure out how to help yourself, go help someone else. Because the energy that we get from helping someone else is unmatchable.

– *Debbie Foster, Managing Partner at Affinity Consulting*

LIVING THE LESSON

- Think about how you can *do a kindness* today. Something seemingly as small as a genuine compliment can make a difference in someone's day and make you feel great at the same time.
- Consider volunteering for a cause or organization that is meaningful to you. Experiment with different ways to get involved and find what works for you.
- Spread the good vibes. Are there things that you and your team can do to give back in a way that's fun, fulfilling, and sincere? Below are just a few ideas. Brainstorm others with your team.
  - Collect toys to bring to kids in the hospital.
  - Visit a nursing home.
  - Mentor a child.

- Adopt a school in your neighborhood.
- Donate clothing.
- Sponsor a food drive for a local food bank.

[24:1] Allan Luks and Peggy Payne, *The Healing Power of Doing Good: The Health and Spiritual Benefits of Helping Others* (Fawcett 1992).
[24:2] Staff, "Volunteering and Mental Wellness." *Project Wellness* (2021). https://projecthelping.org/benefits-of-volunteering/
[24:3] Martin Seligman, *Authentic Happiness: Using the New Positive Psychology to Realize Your Potential for Lasting Fulfillment* (Free Press, 2022).
[24:4] Martin Seligman, *Flourish: A Visionary New Understanding of Happiness and Well-being* (Atria Books, 2011).

Lesson 25

CHOOSE CLIENTS WISELY.

Choice, not chance, determines your destiny.

– *Aristotle*

The importance of working with the right clients is a topic that was covered in the first *50 Lessons for Lawyers* book. We include the topic here because working with the right clients affects more than just your business; it affects your health and well-being. The two most significant aspects of your practice that affect your stress levels, happiness, and sanity are the people you work with and the clients you represent.

You know how it feels when you have the right people working with you, and you're just clicking along. There will always be challenges and deadline pressures, but when you have the right team around you, those challenges and pressures are lessened. The same can also be said for your clients. Regardless of your practice area, when you are working with the right clients, those pressures and deadlines are lessened. If you want to be happier and less stressed, you must be very careful when choosing your clients.

If you were to think of the universe of potential clients and grade them on a scale of A to D, your goal would be to work with only "A" clients. These are the ideal clients for *you*. While there are some universal characteristics of "A" clients, it's important to get very clear about the characteristics of an "A" client for you.

WHAT ARE THE CHARACTERISTICS OF AN "A" CLIENT? YOU GET TO DECIDE

Let's consider some "A" client characteristics that most attorneys would agree on. They pay their bills—on time. They follow your advice. They are polite to your staff, and they're not calling your office every day (or every hour). Although we're speaking in terms of "A" clients, you may also want to think in terms of "A" matters. For example, an "A" matter would fall within the sweet spot for your practice area. It would involve work you enjoy doing, or it might be a matter that has a high likelihood of recovery or a high value.

Have you ever thought about the characteristics of an "A" client or "A" matter for *your firm*? Some lawyers are willing to tolerate extremely difficult clients as long as they pay their bills or the case value is high. Some lawyers simply refuse to put up with demanding clients. The choice is yours. But before you can choose wisely, you must know exactly what an "A" client or matter looks like for *your firm*.

If you've never clearly identified the characteristics of an "A" client or matter for your firm, now is the time. Grab your laptop or pull out a piece of paper and write down a description of your ideal client—your "A" client. Be as specific as you can. Create a picture of your "A" client so that you and everyone on your team know the exact characteristics of an "A" client for your practice.

If you have more than one practice area, write a description of your ideal client for each area. Do the same for what you would consider ideal or "A" matters. Without a crystal-clear picture of who those "A" clients are or what those "A" matters look like, you'll never be able to attract as many of each as you could!

WHAT ARE THE WARNING SIGNS OF A "D" CLIENT? YOU ALREADY KNOW THEM

Okay, now that you know who your ideal clients are, it's time to make room in your practice to accommodate more of them. You can start by not letting any more "D" clients into your practice and letting go of those you already have. And whether or not you want to admit it, you've probably got at least a few "D" clients right now. Caveat: Be aware of your jurisdiction's ethical requirements and always let go of clients ethically, compassionately, and professionally.

Who are these "D" clients? How do you recognize them? You already know the answers to these questions. "D" clients don't pay their bills. They are rude to your team. They may sometimes even be rude to you, but they're always rude to your team. They have unrealistic expectations about their matter. They don't provide the documents you request without follow-up calls and emails. They don't tell the truth. These are just a few of the characteristics of "D" clients. Undoubtedly, you can think of many more. We're also betting that you have a list of warning signs—bells that go off in your head—when a potential "D" client is sitting across the desk from you. Make sure the following warning signs are on your list:

- Arrives late.
- Doesn't bring requested documents.
- Is rude to your receptionist.
- Asks first about price.
- Was referred by a current "D" client.
- Does not listen.
- Is unrealistic about the potential outcome of the matter.
- Is visibly angry or agitated.
- Is currently represented and wants to make a change.

Every lawyer has a "D" client from time to time. But knowing the warning signs of "D" clients isn't enough to keep them out of your practice. Lawyers have an innate desire to help people. So, despite the warning signs, you may agree to represent "D" clients because you *know* you can help them. Or perhaps the business has been a bit slow, so you agree to represent a "D" client because of cash flow pressures. Whatever the reason, you need to say "no" to "D" clients because they will wreak havoc on your practice, your bottom line, and your sanity. And even worse, "D" clients steal from you.

"D" CLIENTS ARE THIEVES

The truth is "D" clients steal from you in two very damaging ways. First, they steal from you by not paying their bills. This theft is insidious because it's not just about the money—it's about the resources wasted trying to collect the money. The phone calls, the emails, the texts. The *aggravation*. The tremendous amount of effort that goes into simply getting paid for the work you've done. Clients who don't pay their bills create incredible stress in the practice and place incredible stress on you. Besides, if you're not going to get paid, wouldn't you rather not get paid for sitting on the beach or golfing or reading a good book than working on your "D" client's case? You should be able to choose the pro bono cases you want to take on—not have them chosen for you.

In addition to stealing your money and resources, "D" clients steal your time. If you examine the cases or matters in your office, there is a very good chance that the 80/20 Rule is at work. The 80/20 Rule essentially says that 80 percent of our results come from 20 percent of our efforts. In your practice, the rule can be expressed this way: 80 percent of your revenues come from 20 percent of your clients. And guess who makes up that 20 percent? Right! Your "A" clients. But don't take our word for it, check your files. The numbers may vary slightly: 75/25 or 70/30. You'll find that the majority of your revenues come from your "A" clients.

Here's another way the 80/20 Rule applies to your practice. Those "D" clients—the 80 percent that generates only 20 percent of your revenue—take up 80 percent of your time and your team's time. They're constantly calling, and your team has to follow up with them about everything from providing documents to paying their bills. On the other hand, those "A" clients—the ones who generate 80 percent of your revenue—respect your time. They provide documents when asked, they don't continually call, email, or text, and they pay their bills. So, what's wrong with this scenario? Your "D" clients are stealing from you. They're stealing the time you could be spending on your "A" clients and getting more of them!

Here's a simple equation to illustrate this point. Let's assume you have 100 clients generating $1 million in revenue. If we apply the 80/20 Rule, the analysis looks like this:

NUMBER OF CLIENTS	TOTAL REVENUE
100 clients	$1 million
20 "A" Clients	$800,000
80 others	$200,000

If you were to increase the number of "A" clients in this equation by 25 percent—just five more clients in this scenario—you could replace all the revenue generated by the 80 others. While the numbers might shift a little, you get the point: stop taking "D" clients so that you can make room in your practice for more "A" clients.

LIVING THE LESSON

- Write down a description of your ideal "A" client(s) and matter(s). Be as specific as you can. Share the descriptions with your team. Make sure everyone understands exactly who an "A" client is for your firm.
- Do the same for "D" clients. Create a list of warning signs for "D" clients. Use the list to create a checklist that you can use as part of your client intake system.
- Pay attention. Sometimes clients can begin to slip from "A" client status during representation. Regardless of the type of case or a client's level of sophistication, they are likely going through a stressful time. If a client begins to slip, by being late paying their bill or is unresponsive to your office, address the matter immediately.
- Analyze the clients you already have. Make a spreadsheet or pull data from your case management program to see whether those clients on whom you're spending the most time are the clients who are generating the most revenue. You might be surprised by what you find!

Lesson 26

WORK LESS.

To do the impossible, you need to ignore the popular.

– Tim Ferriss

We know that you're thinking, "What?! Are you nuts? Work less? How am I supposed to do that? I'm a lawyer; we don't work less." We know. We've been there. We also realize that what we are suggesting might feel antithetical to your work as a lawyer and the culture of many law firms. Stay with us here because many of the lessons in this book will help you work less, stress less, and be happier.

THE AVERAGE LAWYER'S WORKWEEK AND ITS CONSEQUENCES

Before we talk about the potential benefits of working less, let's acknowledge that most lawyers work more than 40 hours a week. Many put in over 50 or even 60 hours a week. Is this sounding painfully familiar? According to the *2018 Legal Trends Report*, "[i]t's not uncommon for lawyers (especially Big Law attorneys) to work up to 80 hours each week."[26:1] That report also found that 75 percent of lawyers reported often or always working outside of regular business hours to catch up on work that didn't get completed during the day or to be available for clients.

Sadly, these statistics are no surprise to practicing lawyers. Long hours, working weekends, and sacrificing your personal life have long been part of the legal profession's culture. Numerous studies have chronicled the health risks of working too many hours—from an increase in coronary artery disease to the likelihood of stroke and poor mental health.[26:2]

We know the research may not surprise you. If you're like most lawyers, you're probably feeling at least some of the effects of the long days. While you may not be able to change the profession's culture, you can make minor adjustments to how you work that can positively impact your physical and mental health and wellness.

We need to think of ourselves as multi-dimensional human beings. It's not just about work-life balance, like two sides of the same coin. Our life is more like a diamond. It's a gem with many different facets, and one of them happens to be work. But there's more to our lives than work. Recognizing that is hard; acting on that is even harder; sustaining it is harder again.

– Jordan Furlong, Author, Founder of Law21

THE RESEARCH

A 2021 study by the World Health Organization (WHO) reported that "working 55 or more hours per week is associated with an estimated 35% higher risk of a stroke and a 17% higher risk of dying from ischemic heart disease, compared to working 35-40 hours a week."[26:3] According to Maria Neira, Director of the Department of Environment, Climate Change, and Health at the WHO, "Working 55 hours or more per week is a serious health hazard. It's time that we all, governments, employers, and employees, wake up to the fact that long working hours can lead to premature death."

The nasty effects of overwork apply not only to the work hours in a week but the work hours in your day. Working more than ten hours a day can contribute to a whole host of physical and mental health issues, including hypertension, heart disease, diabetes, and depression. Long working hours also have an adverse effect on our behavior. People who work long hours are more likely to smoke and increase their use of alcohol. They often exercise less and experience lower sleep quality.[26:4]

Numerous studies have been conducted to determine whether working fewer hours each week can enhance our health, well-being, and happiness. Considering the reported research on working too many hours, you might think that the studies conducted on working fewer hours would all be consistent: to be healthier and happier, we should work fewer hours. However, it's not quite that simple.

A study reported in 2021 by NPR found that "working fewer hours for the same pay led to improved well-being among workers, with no loss in productivity. In fact, in some places, workers were more productive after cutting back their hours."[26:5] Moreover, working fewer hours left people feeling more energized and less stressed. We will admit that this study was conducted in Iceland with a relatively small sample. But it's not surprising given what we know about the detriments of working long hours.

Other studies have found less of a correlation between working hours and a person's overall level of well-being and happiness. Working fewer hours with the same amount of work can actually lead to more stress, not less. Maxed-out workers need less work, not less time to do the same amount of work.[26:6]

And there you have it. Working fewer hours can feel like a recipe for more stress, not less for most lawyers. We think that Wanda Thibodeaux, writing for *Inc. Magazine*, hit the nail on the head.

> *It's not really how much you're working, but why and how. It's context. You can be miserable working 20 hours a week if you're in crappy conditions, or you can be ecstatic working 80 hours because you've got great circumstances.*[26:7]

Yes, context is important. But even if you have found your purpose and love your work and feel that your work as a lawyer is a calling—not merely a job—you must pay attention to the hours you are working and seriously consider cutting back if you need to.

WHAT YOU CAN DO

If you're a sole practitioner or working in a small firm, you have much more control over the hours you work each day and each week. If you're in a larger firm, you'll have less control. But whatever your situation, you do have *some* control. Exercise the control you do have! As we've said throughout this book, you can make small changes. You can take small steps. Those steps add up. You are worth it.

> *When you keep searching for ways to change your situation for the better, you stand a chance of finding them. When you stop searching, assuming they can't be found, you guarantee they won't.*
>
> – FROM *GRIT*, BY ANGELA DUCKWORKTH[26:8]

LIVING THE LESSON

- Because context can be so important to how your work hours affect you, take some time to put your work in context. See *Lesson 5: Get Clear on Your Why.*
- Do you know how many hours you work each day? Each week? If you don't, then start keeping track. We are not talking about billable hours. We are talking about how many hours you work—all of the hours you work.
- Once you know how many hours you work, start looking for opportunities to cut back. You may want to begin by creating a "to-don't" list. See *Lesson 27: Make a To-Don't List.*
- Take small steps and begin to set an example for those around you.

[26:1] Clio, "2018 Legal Trends Report." *Themis Solutions* (2018)
[26:2] Timothy Revell, "Can a shorter working week make us happier?" *Acuity* (December 1, 2018). https://www.acuitymag.com/business/can-a-shorter-working-week-make-us-happier
[26:3] World Health Organization and the International Labour Organization, "Long working hours increasing deaths from heart disease and stroke: WHO, ILO" *WHO and ILO.* (May 17, 2021). https://www.who.int/news/item/17-05-2021-long-working-hours-increasing-deaths-from-heart-disease-and-stroke-who-ilo
[26:4] Kapo Wong, Alan Chan, and S. C. Ngan, "The Effect of Long Working Hours and Overtime on Occupational Health: A Meta-Analysis of Evidence from 1998 to 2018." *International Journal of Environmental Research and Public Health* 16, no. 12 (June 2019). https://doi.org/10.3390/ijerph16122102
[26:5] Andrea Hsu, "Iceland Cut Its Work Week And Found Greater Happiness And No Loss In Productivity." *NPR* (July 6, 2021). https://www.npr.org/2021/07/06/1013348626/iceland-finds-major-success-moving-to-shorter-work-week
[26:6] Timothy Revell, "Can a shorter working week make us happier?" *Acuity* (December 1, 2018) www.acuitymag.com/business/can-a-shorter-working-week-make-us-happier
[26:7] Wanda Thibodeaux, "Your Happiness Isn't Related to Your Work Hours, According to a New Report." *INC Magazine* (December 17, 2018).
https://greatergood.berkeley.edu/article/item/would_working_less_make_you_happier
[26:8] Angela Duckworth, *Grit: The Power of Passion and Perseverance* (Scribner, 2016).

Lesson 27

MAKE A TO-DON'T LIST.

Deciding what not to do is as important as deciding what to do.

– Steve Jobs

What are your typical go-to tasks that somehow get done even when you are overwhelmed with your to-do list? Do you tend to do the easy stuff like setting appointments, making a grocery list, or even spending a lot of time on multiple to-do lists when you intended to do other more complicated tasks? If you do, you know exactly what we are talking about. In our own experience as lawyers and throughout our years helping lawyers, we have repeatedly encountered the phenomenon of actively being unproductive.

When we're bored or faced with uncomfortable tasks, our brains naturally want to avoid those tasks. This concept is covered more fully in *Lesson 19: Identify Your Invisible Saber-Toothed Tigers*. Those easier or less psychologically threatening tasks provide a means for us to feel productive while avoiding the uncomfortable stuff that needs to get done. While you can argue that you are still getting things done, we know all too well that delaying those more uncomfortable tasks comes at a price—increased levels of stress and anxiety. Preemptively identifying and limiting the unnecessary tasks with a to-don't list can help you make more helpful choices when the desire to avoid strikes.

I always taught that you had to do, do, do. But I really believe that we all need to do less. And that's my biggest challenge, doing less yet feeling satisfied

that I'm achieving. So, I have a routine each day. I meditate, then I journal, and then I get to work. I've been pushing myself to do less and find my creativity.
– *Katy Goshtasbi, Branding Expert, Founder of Puris Consulting*

BENEFITS OF A TO-DON'T LIST

Knowing what you shouldn't be doing or don't need to be doing can be very liberating. When you experiment with your to-don't list, you'll be reaping some, if not all, of the benefits below.

- Increases your awareness of unproductive habits.
- Helps to keep you focused on the most critical tasks.
- Improves your efficiency by cutting back on the amount of time and energy your brain spends ping-ponging between different activities (a.k.a. task switching).
- Helps establish and enforce boundaries between your personal and professional time.
- Serves as a signal for when you may be letting psychological discomfort guide your decisions instead of logic.

Simplicity boils down to two steps: Identify the essential. Eliminate the rest.
– *Leo Babauta*

Before starting your to-don't list, we suggest you take a lesson (pun intended) from David Allen, productivity guru and author of *Getting Things Done.*[27:1] Start with your to-do list, and for each item on that list, ask yourself the following questions:

- Does this need to be done by me? If the answer is no, delegate it if you can.
- Do I need to do it? If the answer is yes, move to the next question. If not, cross it off your list.
- Do I need to do it now? If it will take less than two minutes, do it. If not, then schedule time in your calendar to do it.

Be ruthlessly honest in your answers to these questions. Honest answers will begin to create your to-don't list.

ELEMENTS OF A TO-DON'T LIST

Remember that a to-don't list is simply an intentional list of the activities you tend to engage in that drain your energy and delay more important work.[27:2] Your to-don't list will include some specific things. In addition to specific items, your to-don't list will include behaviors you love to engage in when you're avoiding more challenging tasks.

Again, ruthless honesty is key here. If you want to change your behavior, you've got to know where to start.

1. Keep it simple.
2. Keep it short. Limiting yourself to three-to-five items is an excellent place to start.
3. Limit to repeated behaviors.
4.. Keep the list in front of you.

HOW TO CREATE A TO-DON'T LIST

Creating your to-don't list doesn't have to be an onerous task. Start with David Allen's questions and focus on those things you can delegate to others or stop doing entirely. The goal of a to-don't list is to help you find more time to work on things that matter most to you.

Things that matter most must never be at the mercy of things that matter least.

– GOETHE

In addition to specific tasks that you've identified, there are other items that you may want to include on your perennial to-don't list. Some examples are listed below. We're sure you can add your to-don'ts to the list, so have some fun with it.

- Don't check social media until the scheduled time.
- Don't check email until the scheduled time.
- Don't assume that your thoughts are facts.
- Don't proofread emails more than three times.
- Don't (assuming you are working from home) do laundry, clean dishes, dust, make a grocery list, or do other domestic chores until the designated time.

- Don't' check your to-do list or your to-don't list until the scheduled time.

LIVING THE LESSON

- Set a timer for five minutes and make a list of the tasks you tend to do when you are avoiding something. Ask yourself, "Does this need to be done by me? Do I need to do it? Do I need to do it now?"
- Keep a running list for one week and add to it when you notice yourself engaging in a simple task instead of focusing on what you need and intend to get done.
- Pick the top five offenders and put those on your to-don't list.
- Keep your to-don't list physically in front of you as an accountability tool.
- Keep in mind that the goal is progress, not perfection. You will get better as you keep trying.

[27:1] David Allen, *Getting Things Done: The Art of Stress-Free Productivity* (Penguin Books, 2002).
[27:2] Diana Shi, "I tried making a 'to-don't list' instead of a to-do list. Here's what I learned." *Fast Company* (April 6, 2021). https://www.fastcompany.com/90617576/i-tried-making-a-to-dont-list-instead-of-a-to-do-list-heres-what-i-learned

Lesson 28

STOP TOLERATING YOUR TOLERATIONS.

Your life is a reflection of what you tolerate.

– Anonymous

We've all got them, and most of us have many more than we think we do. Tolerations. We can become almost blind to them, even though we may experience them every day. They are typically little things that are simply annoying, yet we continue to tolerate them. You know what we're talking about. It's the dent in your car door that you've been meaning to get fixed. It's that junk drawer, so full of junk you can never get it to close. It's the conversation you need to have with your key assistant that you keep putting off. Tolerations can show up in any aspect of your life—work, family, health, home, finances, and relationships.

Tolerations can seem innocuous. After all, you've probably been tolerating your tolerations for a very long time. They divert your focus and sap your energy and, yes, happiness from your life. Eliminating them can make a big difference in your happiness and sense of well-being.

Getting rid of tolerations is like getting a boost of energy. You already know how good this feels because you have eliminated tolerations in your life, even if you haven't used the word toleration. Eliminating a toleration is like removing a weight from your shoulders. If you're a person who likes to check things off your list, eliminating tolerations can be even more rewarding.

STEP 1 – IDENTIFY YOUR TOLERATIONS

The first step in eliminating tolerations is knowing what they are. Start today by creating your list of tolerations. Let's not make this more complicated than it needs to be. Grab a legal pad and a pen and start jotting down your tolerations. If you're more of a techy and want to use your phone or an app to keep the list, that's fine, too. Just make sure that wherever you keep the list, you know where it is and can easily update it.

What's bugging you? Write down everything that pops into your mind. Don't analyze it. If it's annoying you, write it down. Keep a running list. When you check off your tolerations, continue to add new items to the list. As you get good at this, you may find that the things you're tolerating have taken on a whole new vibe—from "messy junk drawer" to "not getting a weekly massage."

Below are categories to think of as you create your list.

- Health: Doctor, Dentist, Diet, and Exercise
- Work: Environment, Technology, and Staffing
- Home: Interior and Exterior
- Financial: Credit Card Debt and No Financial Plan
- Relationships: Personal and Professional

STEP 2 – START ELIMINATING YOUR TOLERATIONS

As you begin to eliminate your tolerations, keep this in mind: Some tolerations are beyond your control. If one (or more) of your tolerations falls outside your control, you have two choices: you can accept it or reframe it. Is your spouse's annoying habit really that annoying? What about all of their other wonderful qualities that made you fall in love with them in the first place? Focus on those things you can control—or at least influence.

You may want to tackle your easiest tolerations first. Go for the low-hanging fruit! You'll get energy from those small victories that will motivate you to tackle the more significant items on your list. That messy drawer, for example, may only take you ten minutes to clean up, but then every time you open it, you'll smile to yourself with satisfaction.

Some tolerations may require more than a simple step to eliminate. For those tolerations, you can create a list of tasks. If you're tolerating the lack of a financial plan, the first step might be to schedule an appointment with a planner. Whatever the task, take the first step! Don't feel that you have to have every task written out in a plan before acting. There is power in action. Get started!

A year from now you may wish you had started today.

– Karen Lamb

LIVING THE LESSON

- Make a list of your tolerations.
- Start eliminating them.
- Check them off.
- Keep adding to the list and checking things off.
- Celebrate your progress!

Lesson 29

GET ORGANIZED.

For every minute spent organizing, an hour is earned.

– Benjamin Franklin

For some of us, getting organized might not seem relevant. We may *want* to get organized, but when the rubber hits the road, it's low on our priorities. It's easy for organization to fall to the bottom of a to-do list, assuming it was even on there in the first place. Our personal and professional lives can be so demanding that we can barely keep all the fires out, much less organize around them.

While getting organized may seem like a waste of time, science has shown that it's not. Getting organized is associated with much more than a visually tidy space. It can benefit us in a variety of ways, from better health, improved focus and efficiency, to the reduction of harmful stress hormones, like cortisol.

Despite the benefits of getting organized, the case for decluttering isn't entirely clear-cut. Some studies reported by the Mayo Clinic, WebMD.com, and others describe how orderly, clutter-free environments are linked to better overall health and wellness; other studies have found that disorderly environments can promote creativity and fresh ideas.[29:1]

Sometimes the clutter just takes over, like when you're writing a brief and files, papers, and notes are everywhere. It's okay for that kind of clutter to creep in from time to time. In fact, it may indeed help enhance your creative processes. But, for most of us, living in a chaotic and cluttered environment poses more problems than fresh ideas.

If you're thinking, "I like my messy office! My piles of files remind me of what I need to work on!" you should consider the following. Getting organized is what Joseph Ferrari, author of *Still Procrastinating? The No Regrets Guide to Getting it Done,*[29:2] refers to as "Your secret weapon in task completion." According to Ferrari, "You can and must have control over the elements in your environment that cause you to procrastinate." Paradoxically, if those piles of files around your office were actually reminding you to work on them, they wouldn't be there. Instead, those piles of files are helping you procrastinate by reminding you that you're going to work on them tomorrow or maybe next week. So, clean up your office and enlist the help of your staff to keep it organized.

WHY BOTHER?

In addition to boosting your effectiveness, the benefits of an uncluttered environment to our emotional health are well-documented.[29:3] Below are just a few:

- Better focus.
- Higher self-esteem and self-confidence.
- Increased energy.
- Reduced anxiety.
- Reduced stress.

Be honest. When you tidy up your office, don't you feel some of those benefits? Your home office? Even your garage? Despite the benefits, many of us don't even know where to start because we have too much clutter to get through and too little time. It's all too overwhelming, so we just continue to avoid it to our detriment.

GETTING STARTED WITH GETTING ORGANIZED

Getting organized has the potential to carry a lot of emotion with it, so start small. Identify one drawer in your desk or just the desktop, set a timer for ten minutes, then organize that designated area for those ten minutes. If you need to play some music while doing so, go for it. As you go through it, ask yourself the following:[29:4]

- Have I used this within the past year?
- Do I need this anymore?
- Can someone else make better use of this?
- How do I need to store this to confidently know where it is six weeks from now?

It will take a while before you get through everything you wish to organize, but ten minutes a day or a week is a start.

Effective tidying involves only two essential actions:
discarding and deciding where to store things.
Of the two, discarding must come first.
– *Marie Kondō*

LIVING THE LESSON

- Start small by making your bed every day. See *Lesson 42: Make your bed.*
- If you already make your bed every day, start with your desktop. Set a timer for ten minutes and put away anything non-essential, such as the computer screen and keyboard.
- Once you have organized and mostly cleared your desktop, continue by identifying a specific small space to organize and set a timer for ten minutes. Dedicate yourself solely to organizing that space until the timer expires. Repeat this daily until that specific space is organized, then pick your next small space to organize.
- Stick to only one small space at a time.
- To maintain your organization, introduce a quick tidy-up session into your end-of-day routine. Set a five-minute timer and put things back in their dedicated spaces every day.

[29:1] Dan Brennan, "Mental Health Benefits of Decluttering." *WebMD.com* (October 25, 2021). https://www.webmd.com/mental-health/mental-health-benefits-of-decluttering#:~:text=If%20you're%20looking%20for,for%20a%20more%20relaxed%20mind.
[29:2] Joseph Ferrari, *Still Procrastinating: The No Regrets Guide to Getting It Done* (John Wiley & Sons, 2010).
[29:3] Alice Boyes, "6 Benefits of an Uncluttered Space." *Psychology Today* (February 12, 2018). https://www.psychologytoday.com/us/blog/in-practice/201802/6-benefits-uncluttered-space
[29:4] Marie Kondō, *The Life-Changing Magic of Tidying Up: The Japanese Art of Decluttering and Organizing* (Clarkson Potter/Ten Speed, 2014).

Lesson 30

MAKE FRIENDS WITH A TIMER.

Either you run the day or the day runs you.

– Jim Rohn

You know the feeling of too much to do, too little time to do it, and you don't even know where to start. So, you start with the easy stuff and keep putting the toughest tasks, the most time-consuming tasks, the most emotionally burdensome tasks on the back burner. You feel some satisfaction accomplishing these less-threatening tasks, yet those back-burner tasks taunt you day in and day out. You know you need to tackle them because the longer you wait, the more stressful it will be. Yet, you choose to endure the prolonged pain of procrastination in exchange for delaying the perceived discomfort of doing those much-avoided tasks.

We've been there ourselves, as have so many of our clients. It's the bane of a lawyer's existence. The resolution is usually forced upon us by a looming deadline accompanied by a fear of failure or a fear of confirming what we dread most about ourselves (i.e., laziness, incompetence, fraudulence, etc.), even if there is no factual basis for it. It's as if the only path is to delay as much as possible until the deadline is too close to deny. Then we sacrifice whatever is necessary (sleep, relationships, exercise, other work) to get it done.

OUR LAWYER BRAINS AND THE AVOIDANCE OF DISCOMFORT

While problematic and undesirable, we are wired, not just as lawyers but as humans, for this experience. Our brains have evolved to avoid discomfort, whether physical, emotional, real, or imagined. It's a survival mechanism. For more on the brain science of avoidance, see *Lesson 19: Identify Your Invisible Saber-Toothed Tigers*.

OVERCOMING THE PATH OF LEAST RESISTANCE

Each time we learn something new, our brains establish a neuropathway. Think of it as a line connecting point A to point B. Once established, our brains naturally follow the neuropathway. When point A is triggered because, having already been established, the neuropathway to point B is the path of least resistance. Our brains love efficiency, even if it's impractical in our legal work.

It's this path of least resistance that we need to overcome. Our brains will continue to follow the point A to point B neuropathway as the most efficient way to avoid certain tasks until a bigger threat takes priority (i.e., the perceived financial, professional, and social consequences of missing a deadline), or we establish an alternative neuropathway that yields results.

USING A TIMER TO ESTABLISH ALTERNATIVE NEUROPATHWAYS

Using a timer creates an opportunity to establish a new neuropathway while simultaneously decreasing the perceived threat associated with the task. As lawyers, we have all studied for the LSATs, survived law school, studied and passed bar exams, and much more once we eventually got into practice. A timer simply takes the perceived threat of a task you have been avoiding and limits it to, for example, twenty minutes. By using a timer in this way, you limit your perceived potential discomfort from hours or even longer to just twenty minutes. You can handle a little discomfort for twenty minutes. In fact, twenty minutes dedicated to even a challenging task may not feel uncomfortable at all.

When point A is triggered, you have laid a new neuropathway by tolerating this previously avoided discomfort for a short time, demonstrating to your brain that there is more than one path. Once you establish a new neuropathway, you can choose it over the default of avoiding the unpleasant task. The more you choose the alternative neuropathway, the easier it gets to take that path. Choose it enough times, and it becomes the default neuropathway. The original neuropathway weakens and, for some people, disappears entirely.

LIVING THE LESSON

- Set a timer to work on a task you have been avoiding.
    - Set the timer for twenty minutes and focus on just the unpleasant task.
    - If you want to continue at the twenty-minute mark, then set the timer for another twenty minutes.
    - If you have had enough at the twenty-minute mark, move on to another task and revisit the twenty-minute exercise later in the day or the next day.
- Set a timer to maximize your focus and productivity.
    - Identify a specific task you commit yourself to work on, then set a 45-minute timer.
    - Only work on that task for forty-five minutes.
    - At the 45-minute mark, finish the sentence, email, search, etc. that you are doing and set a timer for fifteen minutes.
    - Stand up and walk away from your task for those fifteen minutes and do something unrelated (i.e., stretch, visit the restroom, take a brief walk, listen to music, refill your water).
    - At the fifteen-minute mark, return to your task and once again set the timer for forty-five minutes.
    - Repeat, continuing your original task or with a new task.

Lesson 31

CULTIVATE POSITIVE, SUPPORTIVE FRIENDSHIPS.

Friendship is the most important journey we ever venture on.

– Robin Dunbar, Evolutionary Psychologist

Maybe you've heard people say, "The pandemic has brought out my inner recluse," or "I've turned into a hermit." Maybe you've even felt this way, too. If you do, you are not alone. The pandemic has caused us to feel increased stress, loneliness, and depression. Ironically, it has also caused us to want to withdraw further. On some levels, it's not surprising that we feel this way. We've lived through a time when staying away from others became part of our daily lives. Research has shown that isolation has led to more isolation. Research has also shown that while it's understandable that we can get very comfortable in our cocoon, it's not good for us. Lack of social connections adversely affects everything, from our happiness and well-being to our health and life span.

Friendship takes work. Finding friends,
nurturing friendships, scheduling face time,
it all takes a tremendous amount of work.
But it's worth it. If you put in the effort,
you'll see the rewards of positive friends
who will make your life extraordinary.

– Maya Angelou

In *Growing Young,* Marta Zaraska tells us about studies that show how "building a strong support network of family and friends lowers mortality risk by about 45 percent."[31:1] Not only that, numerous studies and years of research have also documented how cultivating meaningful relationships can improve nearly every aspect of our lives. According to research from the Mayo Clinic,[31:2] friends can:

- Provide support during challenging times.
- Increase your sense of belonging and purpose.
- Improve your self-confidence and self-worth.
- Help you cope with traumas, such as divorce, serious illness, or the death of a loved one.
- Reduce the risk of depression, high blood pressure, and other serious health problems.

Another important aspect of being with our friends is centered in our limbic system. We are literally wired to pick up on the feelings and emotions of those around us. And that leads us to another important aspect of personal connection. Be very careful of the relationships you create and the people you choose to surround yourself with. Your friends will have an influence on your happiness and well-being. Supportive, optimistic, empathic friends will make you feel great.

On the other hand, friends who tend to be negative and thrive on talking about problems and who create (or escalate) drama will likely make you feel not-so-great. We've all experienced what it feels like to be around someone who exudes negative energy. We pick up on it, and we can begin to feel that negativity, too. There is a scientific reason for this. In *Lesson 21*, we talked about the contagiousness of our moods. We are wired to pick up on the emotions of others. So, pay very close attention to the emotions your friends send out to you. And be mindful of your own emotions and how you may be affecting those around you. Send out positive, happy vibes whenever you can, and your friends will pick up on them. They'll also send those vibes back to you, and you'll both be happier as a result.

Let us be grateful to the people who make us happy;
they are the charming gardeners who make our souls blossom.

– Marcel Proust

IN FRIENDSHIP, THINK QUALITY, NOT QUANTITY

In his book, *Friendship in the Age of Loneliness*,[31:3] Adam Smiley Poswolsky provides a guidebook with dozens of suggestions on how to connect with friends—old and new—with a focus on creating quality relationships. His playful approach to making friends will make you smile. While the entire book is worth reading, below are a few suggestions that we think are a great place to start cultivating positive, supportive friendships.

Go Deep Rather Than Wide

Poswolsky quotes Lifeboat's *State of Friendship in America* report[31:4] that found, "It's not about the number of people you associate with. It's about the quality of those relationships."

Pick Up the Phone and Call

When was the last time you picked up the phone and called a friend just to say "Hi!"? Or how about calling one of your best clients just to check in on them? Poswolsky notes, "Being busy isn't an excuse for not staying in touch with the people you care about most."

Build a Healthier Relationship with Social Media

Poswolsky is not a fan of social media, but he realizes that few people are going to give it up. Below are his suggestions to make your social media interactions more meaningful.

- **Real talk beats bragging** – Share lows as well as highs, and be open and honest with your feelings.
- **Open, don't close dialogue** – As Poswolsky points out, social media is not an easy place to disagree. Nuance, tact, and grace are welcome approaches.
- **Promote your friends** – Support their work. Share their accomplishments. Lift them up.
- **Offer compliments** – You don't need to wait for someone's birthday to tell them how wonderful they are!

The pandemic has given us the opportunity to use social media to build real, meaningful friendships. Whether in person or online, to live a happy, fulfilling, long life, as Bette Midler says, "Ya gotta have friends."

I built friendships during the pandemic that I wouldn't have been able to build before. And they are incredible friendships. I feel so lucky that I now have these people in my life that I wouldn't have had if we weren't on social media together all day, every day. Our lives were just too different.

– Ivy Grey, VP of Strategy & Business Development at WordRake

LIVING THE LESSON

- Notice your own emotions and what you are bringing to your friendships. You influence the people around you. Strive to be a positive influence.
- If there are friends in your life who drag you down, take a serious look at those relationships. Do you truly want those people in your life?
- Focus on deepening the positive, supportive friendships in your life.
- Pick up the phone and call a good friend. Right now.

[31:1] Marta Zaraska, *Growing Young: How Friendship, Optimism, and Kindness Can Help You Live to 100* (Random House, 2020).
[31:2] Mayo Clinic Staff, "Friendships: Enrich your life and improve your health." *Mayo Clinic* (January 12, 2022). https://www.mayoclinic.org/healthy-lifestyle/adult-health/in-depth/friendships/art-20044860
[31:3] Adam Smiley Poswolsky, *Friendship in the Age of Loneliness: An Optimist's Guide to Connection* (Running Press, Hachette Book Group, 2021).
[31:4] Alia Mckee and Tim Walker, "State of Friendship in America Report." *Lifeboat* (February 2015). http://www.getlifeboat.com/report

Lesson 32

DO WHAT YOU USED TO DO—PLAY.

We don't stop playing because we grow old; we grow old because we stop playing.

– GEORGE BERNARD SHAW

Play may be the last thing on your list if it even makes the list at all. As adults, it's easy and understandable for play to be relegated to childhood or dismissed as a waste of time. On the contrary, like an athlete's need to recover from strenuous activity, our brains need play to perform at their best.

PLAY IS ABOUT THE PROCESS

Play is anything that engages the imagination, is self-directed, intrinsically motivated, and has boundaries that allow for creativity. It's something you do for the pleasure of doing it and not just for the result.[32:1] For example, play is riding your bike for fun instead of the metrics or playing poker because you enjoy it instead of focusing on winning money. Stuart Brown, the founder of the National Institute for Play, compares play with oxygen when he writes, "It is all around us, yet goes mostly unnoticed or unappreciated until it is missing."[32:2]

René Proyer, a psychologist and researcher in positive psychology and playfulness at Martin-Luther University, Halle-Wittenberg, has identified four types of adult playfulness.[32:3]

1. **Other-Directed** – You enjoy playing with other people.
2. **Lighthearted** – You enjoy improvisation and exploration.
3. **Intellectual** – You enjoy wordplay and problem-solving.
4. **Whimsical** – You enjoy the unusual.

Which playful personality sounds like you? You may be one or all of them. Knowing your type can serve as a tool to help you identify some activities that you might enjoy and others you wouldn't.

The opposite of play is not work. It is depression.
– *Brian Sutton-Smith*

GROWNUPS NEED TO PLAY, TOO

We do not stop benefitting from play just because we are older. Research has revealed that play in adulthood releases endorphins, enhances creativity, forms and deepens relationships, and helps us increase our productivity and maintain our memory and analytical skills. Like meditation, play is a mindfulness exercise that pulls us into the moment and liberates our ruminating minds. Play offers many of the same benefits as mindfulness. Studies have found that play improves our ability to manage stress and helps to alleviate symptoms of anxiety and depression.

HOW TO PLAY

Figuring out how to play can be a challenge. After all, lawyers are accustomed to building our thoughts and behaviors around productivity and metrics. Consider what kind of play personality you most exhibited as a child and start there. Ask yourself this question: "What did I used to enjoy doing that I don't do anymore?" So many lawyers tell us, "I used to like to [fill in your answer], but I just doing have the time to do it anymore." Don't be that person. Do what you used to do. And one last suggestion, don't post about it. Keep it as something for you to enjoy without an expectation of feedback from others.

You do not need to play for hours to reap the benefits. A short amount of play can make a difference. Moreover, play is not the same for everyone. It goes well beyond sports and board games. It can include anything from playing a musical instrument, painting, making jewelry, and woodworking to dancing, exploring nature, and everything in between. Maybe for you, play is getting out on your boat or taking a backroads trip on your Harley. You get to decide how you want to play. And don't be afraid to find tiny moments of play while doing other things.

The truly great advances of this generation will be made by those who can make outrageous connections, and only a mind which knows how to play can do that.
– *Nagle Jackson*

LIVING THE LESSON

- Take a cue from your childhood, such as a love of Play-Doh or Tinker Toys, and consider taking a pottery or woodworking class.
- Build play into your workday. Keep toys on your desk or in your office, so they are there for you when you need a break. We knew a lawyer who practiced juggling during the day. It was a great mental break and a cause for laughter when the balls went flying everywhere.
- Set aside unplanned time on the weekend to get curious about what you are drawn to.
- Explore a park, your neighborhood, or a nature preserve on a bicycle, skates, skateboard, or on foot.
- Dance while making dinner or cleaning.
- Experiment with cooking something new.
- Sing while you are driving.
- Play games such as charades with others.
- Play Sudoku or a crossword puzzle.
- Write a story.
- Doodle.

[32:1] Kristin Wong, "How to Add More Play to your Grown-Up Life, Even Now," *New York Times* (August 14, 2020). https://www.nytimes.com/2020/08/14/smarter-living/adults-play-work-life-balance.html
[32:2] Stuart Brown, *How it Shapes the Brain, Opens the Imagination, and Invigorates the Soul* (New York: Avery, 2009).
[32:3] René Proyer, "A new structural model for the study of adult playfulness: Assessment and exploration of an understudied individual differences variable." *Personality and Individual Differences* 108 (April 2017): 113 – 122. https://doi.org/10.1016/j.paid.2016.12.011

ADDITIONAL RESOURCES

- https://www.journalofplayinadulthood.org.uk
- Dr. Stuart Brown's Ted Talk on Play https://www.ted.com/talks stuart_brown_play_is_more_than_just_fun
- The National Institute for Play http://www.nifplay.org

Lesson 33

SEEK OUT NATURE.

Nature itself is the best physician.

– Hippocrates

"They paved paradise and put up a parking lot." The sadness Joni Mitchell felt when gazing at the juxtaposition of a large, paved parking lot amid Hawaii's green mountains inspired those words in her song "Big Yellow Taxi." We now know that Joni Mitchell's desire for a connection to the beauty of nature runs far deeper than the cultural environmentalist awakening of the late 1960s and early '70s. Recent studies have revealed a strong connection between time spent in nature and well-being. In fact, this research is the genesis for ecopsychology, a new area of social science. Ecopsychology focuses on studying the emotional bond between humans and the earth.[33:1] Let's dig a little deeper.

BEING IN NATURE IS GOOD FOR YOUR HEALTH

The link between nature and our well-being can be dated beyond Hippocrates—across cultures and time. While culturally accepted as a possibility, it's only recently that modern medical research has measured and prescribed how we can benefit most from exposure to nature. Scientific evidence now supports an association between increased psychological well-being and spending time in nature.[33:2]

I love getting outside for some fresh air, sunshine, and vitamin D. When it's hot and sunny and there are butterflies and dragonflies all around. It just makes me feel awesome.

– Renee Stackhouse, Stackhouse, APC, Founder of MSheLE, LLC

Evidence from numerous studies points to links between time spent in nature and a whole range of health benefits.[33:3] Below are just a few:

- Improved cognitive function.
- Improved memory, focus, and creativity.
- Decreased stress.
- Improved mood.
- Increased happiness and subjective well-being.
- Increased sense of purpose.

IT'S EASIER THAN YOU THINK

A 2019 study of 20,000 people led by the University of Exeter found that participants who spent 120 minutes in natural green spaces per week had a higher likelihood of reporting physical and psychological well-being than those who did not meet the 120-minute minimum. [33:4]

We understand that you have demanding personal and professional lives. So, before you dismiss the study and its recommendation by distinguishing yourself from its participants, think about what 120 minutes per week means. That's two hours over the course of a 7-day week—just seventeen to eighteen minutes per day.

Notably, the study found that the minimum of 120 minutes does not need to occur all at once and can be spaced out throughout the week. And you do not need to be in the great wild expanse to reap the benefits. Participants demonstrated the same likelihood of physical and psychological well-being whether the exposure to nature was in a city park or the great outdoors. Moreover, the benefits are not limited to being outside with nature. Studies have also found that simply being around images and sounds from nature can provide psychological and physiological benefits. You can take a mental escape to nature by having beautiful images of nature in your office. According to researchers, simply looking at relaxing images of nature for as little as five minutes can have a calming effect on the brain by activating the parasympathetic system. This can be thought of as a form of mindfulness.

According to Sandra Sgoutas-Emch, a psychological sciences professor at the University of San Diego, "There are studies that show that looking at pleasant images can provide a type of mental escape for individuals during times of moderate stress. For example, a study out of the Netherlands in 2015 found that having students look at pictures of nature helped reduce their stress reaction during a stress test, versus pictures of buildings."[33:5]

Remember, you do not need to go hiking in the great outdoors to help you think and feel better. All you need to do is intentionally choose to engage with nature. You can increase your exposure slowly and steadily. A public park, a simple garden, and a green backyard offer the benefits of nature. You just need to choose it.

There is something infinitely healing in the repeated
refrains of nature—the assurance that
dawn comes after night, and spring after winter.
– RACHEL CARSON

LIVING THE LESSON

- Adopt an easy to care for plant, and have it join you where you spend most of your day.
- Walk through the park instead of around it.
- Stroll through a tree-lined neighborhood.
- Make some exposure to nature an automatic part of your day. Get outside during the day. Even a 10-minute walk at lunchtime can lift your spirits and prime your brain for a productive afternoon.

[33:1] Clark Rector, "Ecopsychology: The Study of Your Relationship to the Natural World." *HealthyPsych* (April 22, 2015).
https://healthypsych.com/ecopsychology-the-study-of-your-relationship-to-the-natural-world/
[33:2] Gregory Bratman et al., "Nature and mental health: An ecosystem service perspective." *Science Advances* (July 19, 2019). https://www.science.org/doi/10.1126/sciadv.aax0903#pill-R33
[33:3] Jill Suttie, "How Nature Can Make You Kinder, Happier, and More Creative." *Greater Good Magazine* (March 2, 2016).
https://greatergood.berkeley.edu/article/item/how_nature_makes_you_kinder_happier_more_creative
[33:4] Jim Robbins, "Ecopsychology: How Immersion in Nature Benefits Your Health." *YaleEnvironment360* (January 9, 2020).
https://e360.yale.edu/features/ecopsychology-how-immersion-in-nature-benefits-your-health
[33:5] Monica Buchanan Piterelli, "Mental escape' pictures actually relieve stress. Here's what they look like." *CNBC* (March 31, 2020).
https://www.cnbc.com/2020/03/31/mental-vacations-and-travel-photos-relieve-stress.html

ADDITIONAL RESOURCES

- Richard Louv, *Vitamin N: The Essential Guide to a Nature-Rich Life*. (Algonquin Books, 2016). https://www.amazon.com/dp/B013JBH888/ref=dp-kindle-redirect?_encoding=UTF8&btkr=1
- Richard Louv, *Last Child in the Woods: Saving Our Children from Nature-Deficit Disorder*. (Algonquin Books, 2008).
- Joni Mitchell, "Big Yellow Taxi." *Ladies of the Canyon* (Reprise, April 1970) https://youtu.be/94bdMSCdw20

Lesson 34

LISTEN TO OTHERS WITH EMPATHY.

Be kind whenever possible. It is always possible.

– *Dalai Lama*

Are you a good listener? A big part of a lawyer's job is listening—listening to clients, opposing counsel, judges, associates, paralegals. But, as lawyers, we're not taught to listen. There's no "Listening 101" in law school. And if there were, it wouldn't be the kind of listening we're talking about here.

While there may not be a "Listening 101" class in law school, lawyers are taught to listen in a very specific way. We're taught to listen so that we can form our response to the other person. We're taught that while we are listening, we need to be crafting our response to what is being said. Lawyers are not the only people who listen like this. Most people do it and don't even realize it. In *The 7 Habits of Highly Effective People*,[34:1] Stephen Covey speaks about how most of us listen and why it's ineffective in so many situations.

> *Most people do not listen with the intent to understand; they listen with the intent to reply. They're either speaking or preparing to speak. They're filtering everything through their own paradigms, reading their autobiography into other people's lives.*
>
> – From *The 7 Habits of Highly Effective People*

Covey speaks about the importance of empathic listening in order to be more effective. He refers to this as listening first to understand and then to be understood. In fact, this concept is one of the seven habits in the book. Listening first to understand will make you a more effective lawyer. But even more than that, research shows us how listening to understand—empathic listening—can also make you a happier person. Listening to the right music can also make you happier. See *Lesson 35: Listen to Music Strategically.*

The kind of empathic listening that Covey writes about is listening that allows you to truly connect with another person. Feeling empathy toward another person involves sensing their emotions and imagining what they may be thinking or feeling. When you are listening empathically, you connect with the other person on a very deep level. You cannot feel empathy toward another person if you are focused on what you are thinking or feeling or how you are going to reply.

Before we go any further, let's clarify the difference between empathy and sympathy, as the two terms can be confused. Here is one of the best distinctions we've seen:

> *The essence of empathy is the ability to stand in another's shoes, to feel what it's like there and to care about making it better if it hurts. . . . When you empathize with someone, you try to see and feel the world from his or her perspective. Your primary feelings are more related to the other person's situation than your own. But when you sympathize, while you understand what others are going through, you don't necessarily feel it yourself right now, though you may be moved to help. Pity—or feeling sorry for someone—similarly captures this idea of recognizing another's pain without simultaneously experiencing a sense of it oneself. With empathy, however, you feel the other person's pain. You're feeling sorry "with" them, not just "for" them.*
>
> – From *Born for Love*[34:2]

At its essence, empathy embodies a sense of kindness toward others. Being kind to others—and to ourselves—is good for our brains and boosts our level of positivity. According to the Mayo Clinic, "Being kind boosts serotonin and dopamine, which are neurotransmitters in the brain that give you feelings of satisfaction and well-being, and cause the pleasure/reward centers in your brain to light up."[34:3]

Listening with empathy is a way to demonstrate kindness to another person. And by demonstrating that kindness to another, you are helping boost your level of happiness. You're also deepening your relationship with that person. You are helping to ease their burden. You are bringing more happiness to their life as well as your own.

Being heard is the psychological equivalent of air.
– RUSSELL GRIEGER

Listening with empathy may require that you unlearn how you were taught to listen in law school. We're not saying there's never a good time to listen like a lawyer. But those times should be limited to when you are lawyering—during depositions, hearings, and trials. When communicating with people in your firm, friends and loved ones, and yes, even your clients, put your lawyer hat aside and listen with empathy. Listen with kindness and a genuine desire to understand. It may take some effort, but it will be worth it. Listening with empathy will make you a better lawyer, a better friend, and a better person. You'll feel better and, yes, happier for it.

I've learned from lawyers that clients don't actually care about whether their lawyer is wearing an expensive suit in a downtown office location. They want to connect with a human being who understands their problems and has empathy for their problems.
– JACK NEWTON, CEO AND FOUNDER OF CLIO

LIVING THE LESSON

- All improvement starts with awareness. If you want to improve your listening skills, you can begin by simply noticing your listening habits. Are you listening like a lawyer with the intent to reply? Notice that and change your mindset.
- Look the other person in the eye and be present.
- Don't interrupt. Don't inject your own story.
- Do your best to listen without judging or evaluating what the other person is saying.
- Ask for feedback from someone who knows you well. Let them know you want to be a better listener. When they give you feedback, listen.

[34:1] Stephen Covey, *The 7 Habits of Highly Effective People* (Simon & Schuster, 1989, 2004).
[34:2] Bruce Perry and Maia Szalavitz, *Born for Love* (HarperCollins, 2010).
[34:3] Steve Siegle, "The Art of Kindness." *Mayo Clinic Health* (May 29, 2020). https://www.mayoclinichealthsystem.org/hometown-health/speaking-of-health/the-art-of-kindness

Lesson 35

LISTEN TO MUSIC STRATEGICALLY.

I would teach children music, physics, and philosophy; but most importantly music, for the patterns in music and all the arts are the keys to learning.

– *Plato*

In his book, *How the Mind Works,* cognitive psychologist Steven Pinker describes music as "auditory cheesecake." According to Pinker, "Cheesecake packs a sensual wallop unlike anything in the natural world because it is a brew of mega doses of agreeable stimuli, which we concocted for the express purpose of pressing our pleasure buttons."[35:1] That's a mouthful.

Music works like a mix of drugs that trigger multiple pleasure circuits in our brain. Just as our bodies need food and water to satisfy our hunger and thirst, our brains need music to satisfy our need for connection and meaning. Emerging research suggests that we can even use music to impact our brainwaves.

MUSIC AS MEDICINE

The idea of music as medicine is discussed in the writings of Aristotle and Plato and dates back to various cultures long before them. While the earliest known reference to music as therapy in modern times appeared in a medical journal in the early 1800s, music's role in American medicine didn't take root until the 20th century. It wasn't until musicians began playing for wounded veterans in hospitals after World War II that doctors noted patients' physical and emotional responses to music. As a result, they advocated for the development of a curriculum for music therapy to be used in the field of medicine. Since then, music therapy has been routinely used to help lower blood pressure, improve respiration, reduce heart rate, and relax the muscles. It is employed to relax patients before and after surgery and reduce recovery time from a stroke. Going well beyond the physical benefits, music is also used to improve mental health and overall brain function.

Research reported at PositivePsychology.com[35:2] found that music therapy has six specific benefits:

1. Reduces anxiety and physical effects of stress.
2. Improves healing.
3. Can help manage Parkinson's and Alzheimer's disease.
4. Reduces depression and other symptoms in the elderly.
5. Helps reduce symptoms of psychological disorders, including schizophrenia.
6. Improves self-expression and communication.

YOUR BRAIN ON MUSIC

Research has found that listening to music impacts neurochemicals such as dopamine, often associated with our pleasure centers; cortisol, which plays a role in our fight-or-flight response; serotonin and other hormones involved in immunity; and oxytocin, which helps foster connection to others.

Improved Mood

Music's impact on the brain includes an influence on our mood. The dopamine released in the brain after fifteen minutes of listening to music leads to the experience of a natural high. It's a neurotransmitter that leads to increased feelings of happiness and excitement. Other neurochemicals, such as serotonin and norepinephrine, are also released, similarly acting as natural anti-depressants and even invoking feelings of euphoria.

Improved Learning and Memory

Music can help you learn and improve your memory because of how it stimulates your brain. Researchers have found that when performing memory tests, subjects who listened to classical music outperformed those who worked in silence or listened to white noise. Those subjects who listened to classical music when attempting simple processing tasks such as matching numbers to shapes were also able to outperform those who didn't. Specifically, Mozart helped participants complete these tasks faster and more accurately.

GET STRATEGIC WITH BINAURAL BEATS

Going beyond neurochemicals, scientists are now also studying how music impacts our brain waves. Emerging research has found that the strategic use of binaural beats can positively impact memory, mood, performance, creativity, and sleep. Binaural beats are technically not music in the way that we know it. Rather, they are the resulting sound perceived by your brain when each of your ears hears a slightly different frequency. Your brain is compensating for the disparity in frequencies by perceiving its own third sound. When sustained over time, binaural beats can synchronize with your brain waves and even alter your brain wave activity.

When listening, make sure you have distinct sounds entering each ear, as your brain needs two different frequencies to perceive the third binaural frequency. Listening through both headphones or both earbuds is necessary to achieve this. If listening ambiently or if an earbud falls out, you will not hear the binaural beats created by your brain.

You can strategically play binaural beats to encourage brain waves specific to how you want to feel. For example, listen to gamma or beta wave frequencies when you need to focus at work. Listen to alpha waves when you need to tap into your creativity. And listen to theta or delta frequencies when you need to relax and get ready for bed. If you want to experiment with binaural beats, you can search most music apps for the type of beat you're looking for.

MUSIC CONNECTS YOU WITH OTHERS

Music connects us through feelings and experience by multiplying the individual benefits—another trigger for those feel-good hormones. Music's role is so ingrained in our societies that we may not even realize its connective role in our everyday lives. National anthems connect thousands at sporting events, hymns build a common identity in religious groups, and lullabies foster secure attachments between caregivers and babies, just to name a few. This feeling of connection to others is an integral part of our well-being.

LIVING THE LESSON

- Listen to upbeat music in the morning. You can encourage your "get up and go" hormones by playing light and pleasant music shortly after you wake up.

- Play soothing music such as classical, soft rock, or nature relaxation sounds (i.e., waves crashing, wind in the trees, wind chimes, etc.) to help you focus. Mozart is an excellent place to start.
- To reconnect with old feelings and memories, play music from that era in your life. Music memory resides in the part of your brain that is least affected by the triggers of memory loss. Music is one of the quickest and easiest ways to time travel.
- Be intentional about your listening. Too much of a good thing is still too much. So, make sure to take breaks from listening to music so that your brain can sense a definite distinction between the therapeutic tones throughout the day. Also, be discriminating with your choice of music. Fast beats and hard rock can be fun and effective when you want an energy boost, but the quickened heartbeat they elicit can generate a message of anxiety in the brain if listened to for extended periods.

[35:1] Steven Pinker, *How the Mind Works* (W. W. Norton & Company, 1997).
[35:2] Heather Craig, "What are the Benefits of Music Therapy?" *PositivePsychology.com* (June 12, 2021). https://positivepsychology.com/music-therapy-benefits/

Lesson 36

GET YOUR BUTT UP AND OUT OF THAT CHAIR.

When it comes to health and well-being, regular exercise is about as close to a magic potion as you can get.

– THICH NHAT HANH

Yes, that's right, we said it (well, more accurately, Thich Nhat Hanh said it)—regular exercise is like magic for our well-being, yet not for the reasons you may think. The common adage, "Movement is medicine," is often applied to physical health. While undeniably true, we are focusing on what recent studies have found—exercise has a direct impact on mental health and even your performance at work.

SHOULD VERSUS WHY

Before we get into the seemingly magical powers of exercise, let's take a moment to challenge how we typically think about exercise. Understandably, most of us view exercise as a *should.* That messaging is prevalent throughout our culture. We have decades of studies providing evidence supporting the *should* for exercise. Yet, we are rarely, if ever, challenged to ask ourselves *why* exercise (and its benefits) even matter to us.

Without a personal connection to the *why* we are more likely to give up when our motivation dwindles. See *Lesson 9: Give Up on Motivation*. The "I *should* exercise because (insert your obligation here)" is a powerful de-motivator. When exercise is another thing to get done in our already overscheduled, overwhelmed lives, it will never be as attractive as scrolling on your phone or binge-watching TV for so-called relaxation. Once we acknowledge and accept that acting based on a *should* will not be enough for sustainable change (if it were, we would all be super-fit specimens of peak physical abilities), we can push past cultural norms and consider the *why*.

Our *whys* are more powerful than our *shoulds* because they are closely connected to our values. See *Lesson 5: Get Clear on Your Why*. Why do you want to feel, look, or be better? Better health is great, but *why* do you want to experience better health? That's where the key lies. Each of us has a unique set of *whys,* such as:

- Stress release because you value connection and want to be more present with your friends and family after work.
- Disease management and prevention because you want to feel good and have an active relationship with the people you love.
- Mitigating your fight-or-flight response because you value service, and so you can think more clearly in stressful situations.

The *whys* cannot be solely dictated by science or culture. They are *your* unique drivers.

YOUR BRAIN ON EXERCISE

An often-parodied anti-drug PSA from the late '80s used the example of someone frying an egg to illustrate the impact of drugs on the human brain "This is your brain. This is drugs. This is your brain on drugs. Any questions?" (10 points if you remember it, or go look it up.) If we attempted that PSA using your brain on exercise, that infamous egg would turn into a technicolored superhero chicken with a big smile. Research can now confirm for us what the ancient Greeks such as Herodicus, Hippocrates, and Galen already knew; exercise strengthens the mind in three very specific ways.[36:1]

Anti-Depressive Impact

Exercise has been found to increase serotonin levels in the brain, the same neurotransmitters targeted by pharmaceutical antidepressants. Research has shown that patients with major depressive disorders benefited as much from exercise as they did from anti-depressants, and those patients who continued to exercise maintained lower depression rates a year later when compared to those who were less active.[36:2]

Mood Enhancement

Exercise helps those who are significantly depressed, but what about the rest of us? Research has also found that the average person experiences an improvement in mood about five minutes into moderate exercise.

Respond More Effectively to Stressors

Exercise doesn't just help lift your mood on a stressful day. It can also change how your brain responds to stressful situations in the future. This is especially critical for lawyers. The legal profession is inherently adversarial in nature. It is designed to challenge instead of support. A lawyer's entire legal career, by design, is filled with perceived threat after perceived threat. That opposing counsel challenging your every move is more than just a nuisance. To your brain, those challenges are a potential threat to your survival. Our adversarial system puts a lawyer's brain under constant assault. Combine the adversarial nature of your work with the inherent human reactions of fight-or-flight, and you have a serious need for managing how you respond to stressors.

The more time I spend exercising—hiking, yoga, long dog walks—the more it allows my brain to do the things that are important and to find solutions and to think about the future and plan. I think that exercise helps me free up brain space, and get away from all of the busy, busy, busy. As a result, I'm more productive now than I've ever been, and at the same time, I'm healthier than I've ever been.

– *Patrick Palace, Founder of Palace Law and Palace Personal Injury Law Group*

Exercise Can Reprogram Your Brain

While it was previously believed that the brain stopped changing after about age 25, recent studies have blown that theory out of the water. The brain can and does continue to change throughout our lives. This is referred to as neuroplasticity. More interestingly, studies have now confirmed that we can intentionally change the structure and function of our brains.

We know that fight-or-flight is a natural reaction to a perceived threat. See *Lesson 3: Why Resilience Matters*. Exercise can change what a fight-or-flight response means for our brains. When we exercise, especially cardiovascular exercise, our bodies go through many of the same physical responses as when we experience an anxiety or panic attack. Our hearts pump faster, and we breathe more rapidly to get oxygenated blood to our muscles more efficiently.

Our muscles tense up, and our focus narrows in preparation for acute physical exertion.

Okay, so *why* should we mimic a stress response when trying to reduce stress? Say it with us—neuroplasticity! Our brains aren't just wired to protect us from perceived threats in the moment. They are also wired to adapt. By triggering the physical symptoms of fight-or-flight through exercise in a way that regularly results in a serotonin increase yet doesn't involve a perceived threat to our "survival," we change how our brain manages a stress-related response.

Recent studies have found that exercise helps associate (physical stress) symptoms with safety instead of danger. What does this mean for us? When our fight-or-flight response is triggered, we can more easily disengage from the stress response and re-engage intentional, logical thinking because physical fight-or-flight experiences are no longer directly associated with a threat. As such, our brains more quickly redistribute resources to other areas, such as the pre-frontal cortex, allowing us to engage in the executive functioning we so intensely rely on in our work. In this way, through exercise, we can intentionally change the structure and function of our brain.

CLASSIC STRESS RESPONSE

Perceived Threat → Physical Stress Symptoms

- One neural pathway connecting stress symptoms and perceived threat

EXERCISE STRESS RESPONSE

Lack of Perceived Threat → Physical Stress Symptoms

- One neural pathway connecting stress symptoms and perceived threat
- One neural pathway connecting stress symptoms and lack of perceived threat

NEUROPLASTICITY

Physical Stress Symptoms → Lack of Perceived Threat

By creating a neural pathway connection through exercise associating stress symptoms without a perceived threat, we establish an alternative for our brains to consider as a reason for experiencing those physical stress symptoms—something that is NOT a threat. As a result, we change how our brain responds to stress by exposing it to stress-like conditions.

LOOK FOR THE HIDDEN IMMEDIATE GRATIFICATION

Our culture tends to focus on the physical benefits of exercise. While well-founded, these physical benefits are usually not evident for a while. Most of us must wait to see the benefits of our exercise routines on our bodies. This often results in a lack of motivation to continue because it misses our need for immediate gratification.

This is where an understanding of our brain chemistry can be useful. That mood boost we experience about five minutes into moderate exercise can be a source of immediate gratification. Suppose we seek it and knowingly experience it right away. In that case, we are more likely to associate exercise with a positive experience that we want to return to, rather than the need to wait for the benefits to show up on a scale. One way to remind yourself of the immediate positive effects of exercise when you don't feel like doing it is to ask yourself the question, "Will I feel better after I exercise?" The answer to that question is almost always, "Yes!"

CHECK YOUR EGO

We are willing to bet that you didn't get where you are today by thinking small. No, that high achiever mindset of yours drove you to set your sights high and push hard right out of the gate. While effective in certain areas of life, this approach can be counterproductive when starting and maintaining an exercise routine. Starting too intensely can be a deterrent because it shortens the release of serotonin and our ability to enjoy it by pushing us too fast into physical exhaustion. If we hold back our ambitious nature a bit and accept the pursuit of a much smaller goal, we can both have our proverbial cake and eat it too. We can both enjoy the immediate results of a mood boost and maintain that enjoyment long enough to reap the physical benefits.

LIVING THE LESSON

- Check your ego and start small. Initiate your exercise routine like a true beginner and work your way to more demanding exercises over time. Try starting with a fifteen-minute brisk walk three times per week. After four weeks, make it a twenty-minute walk. On week nine, increase it to thirty minutes. Over time, you can increase the frequency, intensity, or both by adding another workout, jogging, or cycling instead of walking. Eventually, you could add on other workouts, such as resistance training with floor work (push-ups, sit-ups, squats, planks, etc.) or light weightlifting.

- Focus on how good it feels to move instead of the end goal of the physical change. Take note of how you feel just before you start exercising and compare that to how you feel when you finish exercising. Keep a brief log of each before and after, really focusing on how you feel emotionally. Do you notice a pattern?
- Get out your pen and paper (yes, we are going old school here), set a five-minute timer, and write out your *whys* for exercise. Leave out the *shoulds*. See *Lesson 5: Get Clear on Your Why* and *Lesson 45: Rekindle Your Friendship with Pen and Paper.*

[36:1] Michael Grant, *A Short History of Classical Civilization* (London: Weidenfeld and Nicolson, 1991).
[36:2] Kirsten Weir, "The Exercise Effect." *American Psychological Association* (December 10, 2011). https://www.apa.org/monitor/2011/12/exercise

Lesson 37

LET YOUR GUARD DOWN.

I'm a lawyer—we eat vulnerability for breakfast.

– From Daring Greatly by Brené Brown

When was the last time you felt vulnerable? Wait. Before you answer that question, let's talk about what we mean by being vulnerable. The word vulnerable is derived from the Latin verb *vulnerare,* which means "to wound." As the word evolved, its meaning shifted to "capable of being physically wounded." Today, the Merriam-Webster Dictionary defines vulnerable as "easily hurt or harmed physically, mentally, or emotionally." Historically, vulnerability or being vulnerable has been perceived as weakness. After all, if you can be hurt or wounded by someone else, doesn't that make you the weaker person?

Brené Brown, research professor, author, and widely-cited expert on the subject of vulnerability, defines vulnerability as "uncertainty, risk, and emotional exposure."[37:1] Think about that definition for a moment. Would you consider someone willing to face uncertainty, risk, and emotional exposure weak?

It takes a good bit of strength and courage to allow ourselves to be vulnerable. Vulnerability is actually the opposite of weakness. It is strength, courage, and fearless authenticity. Brown describes vulnerability as "the birthplace of love, belonging, joy, courage, empathy, and creativity."

> *Vulnerability is the core of all emotions and feelings. To feel is to be vulnerable. To believe vulnerability is weakness is to believe that feeling is weakness. To foreclose on our emotional life out of a fear that the costs will be too high is to walk away from the very thing that gives purpose and meaning to living.*
>
> – FROM *DARING GREATLY*

Now, let's revisit that question about the last time you felt vulnerable. Was it before you had to deliver bad news to a client? Was it when you decided to finally have that difficult conversation with your law partner? Was it when you were standing in front of a jury awaiting their verdict? Maybe it was a time when you faced uncertainty, risk, or emotional exposure in your personal life. Whenever it happened, it was not a time of weakness. You may have been uncomfortable, but you were not weak. Again, Brené Brown's words in *Daring Greatly* are eloquent: "Vulnerability sounds like truth and feels like courage. Truth and courage aren't always comfortable, but they're never weakness." The enigmatic thing about vulnerability is that it can feel like weakness to us, while those around us see courage.

> *If you choose to be vulnerable with another person, that's not a sign of weakness. It's a conscious choice that requires courage.*
>
> – FROM *MIND OVER MOMENT: HARNESS THE POWER OF RESILIENCE*[37:2]

In his book, *Bring Your Whole Self to Work,*[37:3] Mike Robbins outlines five specific strategies to be more successful, effective, and engaged at work. Foundational to all of them is authenticity, and foundational to authenticity is vulnerability. In an article published in *Greater Good Magazine,*[37:4] Robbins cites a study published in the *Journal of General Management* which found that "more authentic leaders tend to engage in active, constructive conflict behaviors—things like widening the lens to consider alternate viewpoints . . . being authentic is essential to resolving conflict at work in a productive and positive way."

BENEFITS OF VULNERABILITY

Despite the research around vulnerability, it's not easy for most of us—especially lawyers—who may be afraid to show any perceived weakness. But as the research has shown, while vulnerability may feel like weakness, it's not weakness. It takes courage to be vulnerable, and that courage builds strength, which can benefit both your personal and professional life.

- Vulnerability can help ease anxiety, build resilience and lead to less burnout. Allowing ourselves to acknowledge and experience difficult emotions is a signal to our brain that we can deal with these emotions.
- Being vulnerable builds trust—a key component of emotional intelligence. Building trust helps us connect with others and strengthens our relationships. It helps to humanize us, and it not only makes us better lawyers; it makes us better people.
- Vulnerability can increase self-awareness. Acknowledging our emotions is key to self-awareness. Being self-aware is the first step in managing our emotions and not being controlled by them.
- Embracing vulnerability and authenticity can help us get better at resolving conflict more constructively and broaden our thinking to include alternate viewpoints—both essential skills for effective lawyers.

Kevin O'Keefe, CEO and Founder of LexBlog, Inc., is a trial lawyer turned legal-tech entrepreneur. He is a perfect example of what it means to be open and authentic. His authenticity makes you feel as though you know him, even if you've never met, and it's helped him grow LexBlog into a community of over 30,000 legal professionals from around the world. "Lawyers are afraid to be vulnerable," says O'Keefe. "If they let their guard down, others may think less of them. The community may think less of them. When you let your guard down and do something different, you may not know how it's going to work out, but that's okay. Be vulnerable and have faith that it always works out. It does."

A BEAUTIFUL MESS

Vulnerability has been referred to as a beautiful mess because it brings significant risks and big rewards. It can feel scary and alone, while at the same time, it can be the start of a path to new relationships. It can lead to greater emotional strength and the ability to lessen burnout—especially in jobs that can take an emotional toll on us. Whether you are a lawyer with years of experience, a new law school grad preparing to take the bar exam or a 1L waiting for your first set of grades—the law can take an emotional toll on you. Let your guard down.

We love seeing raw truth and openness in other people, but we are afraid to let them see it in us.

– Brené Brown

LIVING THE LESSON

- The first step is to simply start observing your emotions. No judgment here. Just observe what you are feeling—anger, sadness, or anxiety—without thinking about it or acting on it.
- The next step is acknowledging your emotions. Remind yourself it's okay to feel what you're feeling.
- Decide whether to take the risk and share how you are feeling.
- If you decide not to take the risk, that's okay. But keep challenging yourself to let your guard down.

[37:1] Brené Brown, *Daring Greatly: How the Courage to Be Vulnerable Transforms the Way We Live, Love, Parent, and Lead* (Penguin Random House, 2012).

[37:2] Anne Grady, *Mind Over Moment: Harness the Power of Resilience* (Anne Grady, 2020).

[37:3] Mike Robbins, *Bring Your Whole Self to Work* (Hay House, 2018).

[37:4] *Mike Robbins,* "How to Bring Your Whole Self to work." *Greater Good Magazine* (September 19, 2018). https://greatergood.berkeley.edu/article/item/how_to_bring_your_whole_self_to_work

Lesson 38

MOVE IN SYNC WITH OTHERS.

There are shortcuts to happiness, and dancing is one of them.

– Vicki Baum

Have you ever found yourself moving to the rhythm of a song and then noticing someone else moving in the same rhythm? What kind of feeling did that bring up for you? How about that feeling at a concert when everyone is singing, rocking back and forth at the same time? For most of us, the experience is a positive one, and that is no coincidence. In those moments, you're experiencing the power of interpersonal synchrony. Interpersonal synchrony is defined as "the spontaneous rhythmic coordination of actions, emotions, thoughts, and physiological processes across time between two or more individuals."[38:1] In those moments, you're *in sync* with those around you.

THE SCIENCE OF SYNCHRONIZING WITH OTHERS

Long before Martha and The Vandellas had us "Dancing in the Streets," people around the world and across cultures have gotten together in group settings to perform music and dance. Scientists theorize from an evolutionary biology perspective that this shared attraction to music and synchronized movement may have facilitated the important function of encouraging social bonding and cooperation. More specifically, researchers argue that this sense of connection from synchronous movement is affiliated with neurohormones such as endorphins. The endorphins experienced from physical activity become associated with the people we are with and encourage social bonding.

THE BENEFITS OF SYNCHRONY

You guessed it. Moving in synchrony with other people supports your sense of well-being and happiness. It's fun! Singing and dancing with others is a positive cross-cultural experience. In fact, research has found that "moving in synchrony with other persons has positive effects on cooperation, helpfulness, trust, closeness, and empathy."[38:2] Being in sync with another person is good for both of you.

SYNCHRONY AT WORK

In addition to the positive, upbeat feelings we get from being in sync with others in our personal lives and social settings, research tells us that synchrony at work can help build stronger, flexible, more resilient teams.[38:3] In general, people enjoy being in sync with each other. When we are in sync with each other at work, everyone feels less stressed and more productive. We know you've experienced this from time to time. Haven't there been times when you and your team were working to beat a deadline or close a deal, and despite the pressure, you enjoyed yourself? If you answered yes, then you and your team were in sync with each other, and that synchrony helped create a sense of flow for everyone.

Flow, like synchrony, feels great. In his book *Flow: The Psychology of Optimal Experience,*[38:4] Mihaly Csikszentmihalyi explains that our level of happiness can be increased by being in flow. He defines flow as "a state in which people are so involved in an activity that nothing else seems to matter; the experience is so enjoyable that people will continue to do it even at great cost, for the sheer sake of doing it." The more often you can experience flow, the more productive, effective, and happy you'll be.

HOW TO SYNCHRONIZE WITH OTHERS

Okay, back to dancing. Before you allow those scenes from *Footloose* playing in your mind to dissuade you from the idea of getting in sync with others, take note that dancing is just one example of synchronized movement. It's really just about doing the same movement at the same time. Simple movements such as walking, synchronized finger tapping, nodding in agreement, rocking, arm movements, and exercise provide the same benefits.[38:5]

So, there you have it. Interpersonal synchronization—being in sync with others—supports your happiness and well-being. It supports theirs, too.

And in the workplace, being in sync with others increases the feeling of flow, making even intense work much more enjoyable. You don't have to dance in the hallways to experience these feelings, but you just might want to.

LIVING THE LESSON

- Participate in an exercise class virtually or in person.
- Coordinate synchronized walking with a friend. Just walk. Don't talk.
- Take a dance class.
- Take a yoga class.

[38:1] Ilanit Gordon, "What is Synchrony and Why is it Important." *Psychology Today* (June 12, 2020). https://www.psychologytoday.com/us/blog/the-biology-bonding/202006/what-is-synchrony-and-why-is-it-important
[38:2] Shahram Heshmat, "Social Benefits of Synchronization." *Psychology Today* (December 31, 2021). https://www.psychologytoday.com/us/blog/science-choice/202112/social-benefits-synchronization#:~:text=Research%20finds%20that%20moving%20in,produces%20positive%20attitudes%20toward%20them.
[38:3] Sally Blount and Sophie Leroy, "The Synchronous Leader: How Social Synchrony Impacts Teams" *Human Synergistics International* (November 29, 2016). https://www.humansynergistics.com/blog/culture-university/details/culture-university/2016/11/29/the-synchronous-leader-how-social-synchrony-impacts-teams
[38:4] Mihaly Csikszentmihalyi, *Flow: The Psychology of Optimal Experience* (Harper Perennial Modern Classics, 2008).
[38:5] Malia Wollen, "How to Get In Sync With Someone." *New York Times* (November 24, 2020). https://www.nytimes.com/2020/11/24/magazine/how-to-get-in-sync-with-someone.html

Lesson 39

RECOVERY IS ESSENTIAL FOR AN ATHLETE'S PERFORMANCE. YOURS, TOO.

Remember, often doing less is far more powerful than doing more.

– *Sage Rountree*

Athletes understand the importance of recovery for peak performance. Marathon runners don't run marathons every day. Professional tennis players don't compete in tournaments every week, nor do golfers. Pick your sport; most elite athletes in any sport know the dangers of overtraining. Overtraining, not allowing for adequate recovery, can eventually develop into overtraining syndrome that results in chronic fatigue and declining performance. Once overtraining syndrome sets in, it can be difficult to reverse.

In an interview published in the *Journal-Advocate*, Karin VanBaak, a sports medicine physician, explains, "People who over-train often have trouble with performance. Maybe they're getting a lot more fatigued from a sports activity that used to be easy for them. They may even be getting more tired in their regular lives outside of sports. They may be dealing with mental burnout or a lack of interest in a sport they used to enjoy."[39:1] VanBaak is describing overtraining syndrome in athletes, yet the symptoms she's describing are the very same challenges most lawyers are faced with: fatigue, depression, poor sleep, feeling more tired at the office *and* out of the office, burnout, and a lack of interest in things they used to enjoy. Sound familiar?

In her book, *The Athlete's Guide to Recovery*, Sage Rountree explains, "When you're wound tightly, for whatever reason, you don't get the downtime you need to bring your body into balance. Add this to the fatigue you're already carrying due to your training, and it's a recipe for disaster."[39:2] Like the athletes Rountree describes, far too many lawyers simply don't get the downtime they need. They are running endless marathons. They are working all the time. They work long days. They work at night. They work on the weekends. They don't take vacations. They are too busy being busy to relax. Maybe you are one of them. If you are, you must stop overtraining and start incorporating recovery into your life. Sometimes, as counterintuitive as it may sound, doing less is far more powerful than doing more.

WHAT IS RECOVERY?

At its essence, recovery is time that allows your body to heal after a workout. When you train, you are stressing your muscles and cardiovascular system. This stress damages your muscles by creating microtears, tiny injuries to your muscle fibers. These microtears created in your workout make you stronger. But it is not the workout alone that makes you stronger. The time after your workout—during recovery—allows those microtears to heal. And when they do, they create stronger muscles than they were before.

In order to see gains in fitness, in order for the body to keep doing what you want it to do, you have to give it enough rest to repair itself.

– Karin VanBaak, in the Journal-Advocate

Athletes need recovery to get stronger and more fit. You need recovery to be at your be your best. But many lawyers are running marathons day after day after day. If you're not making time for recovery, you are overtraining. Overtraining, never-ending work, and constant stress will lead to injury. You know this already because you're living it. But there is something you can do about it.

BUILD ACTIVE RECOVERY INTO YOUR DAY

In *Lesson 3*, we talked about the importance of taking breaks throughout the day to build micro-resilience. These breaks can be very short—as little as 30 seconds every 30 minutes can make a difference. You can also take longer breaks of two to three minutes every ninety minutes.

These short breaks throughout the day are what athletes refer to as active recovery. Active recovery can occur *during* a workout. In interval training, athletes push themselves for a specific period; they allow themselves to rest for a set period. A cyclist, for example, may push really hard for ten minutes, lower the intensity for a few minutes, then push again for ten minutes.

When athletes lower the intensity, they're not stopping completely. They're giving their body a chance to relax and reset before they dial up the intensity again. These moments of active recovery keep them fresh for the higher intensity work. Look for ways you can incorporate active recovery into your workday.

BUILD RECOVERY INTO YOUR WEEK AND BEYOND

You can also build active recovery into your weekly routine by taking a rest day. A rest day for the lawyer-athlete means not working. Unplugging. Resting completely. We're not suggesting that you need to lie on the sofa all day on your rest day. Your rest day can be an active recovery day. It can be your day to do whatever you want to do.

In addition to including active recovery during your workday and incorporating a rest day during the week, sometimes you just need a complete break. These breaks can be days or weeks in length and are essential to avoid overtraining and the dangers it presents. Athletes refer to these complete breaks from training as long-term recovery. You can refer to them as vacations. Yes, vacations. Plural. Throughout the year. Away from the office. Away from the work. Your mind and your body need breaks throughout the year.

SLEEP! YOUR RECOVERY SUPER-POWER

Experts agree that perhaps the most important form of recovery is sleep. See *Lesson 17: Get Enough Sleep*. Lack of sleep negatively impacts everything from cognitive performance and immune system to mental health. Regardless of how much active recovery you incorporate into your days or how many rest days or vacations you take, your overall health will suffer if you're not getting enough quality sleep.

> *If you do not get enough sleep each night, you'll accrue "sleep debt," for which your body will eventually demand repayment. Plentiful sleep should be a key feature of your recovery plan.*
>
> – From *The Athlete's Guide to Recovery: Rest, Relax, and Restore for Peak Performance*

So now you know. You may not have realized it before, but you are an athlete. Your arena is your office. Your training is your work. You must take control of how you train and how you recover in order to be in peak condition. Recovery is an essential component of your training.

LIVING THE LESSON

- Set reminders throughout your day for active recovery breaks.
- Make sure you are getting enough quality sleep. This is absolutely essential to your health and well-being on every level you can imagine.
- Go to your calendar right now and block off *at least* two weeks in the coming year for long-term recovery. These don't need to be consecutive weeks, but they do need to be out of the office—away from work.
- Now, get busy planning the vacation you just scheduled. The anticipation of the experience will make you feel great. And when you feel great, you'll be more focused and productive for your training . . . um, we mean work.

[39:1] UCHealth Staff, "Rest and recovery are critical for an athlete's physiological and psychological well-being." *Journal Advocate* (February 10, 2022). https://www.journal-advocate.com/2022/02/10/rest-and-recovery-are-critical-for-an-athletes-physiological-and-psychological-well-being/
[39:2] Sage Rountree, *The Athlete's Guide to Recovery: Rest, Relax, and Restore for Peak Performance* (VeloPress, 2011).

Lesson 40

PRACTICE A REGULAR SCREEN FAST.

People who smile while they are alone used to be called insane, until we invented smartphones and social media.

– Mokokoma Mokhonoana

What would it feel like to be entirely without screens for a day? Can you remember the last time, if ever, that you experienced that? While the practice of law, and we as its practitioners, continue to benefit from technological advances, this does not come without a price. For many lawyers, just talking about avoiding screens brings about feelings of both anxiety and yearning. We can identify the negative impact of looking at screens all day, yet we simultaneously fear the perceived consequences of not doing so.

THE PHYSICAL IMPACT OF SCREENS

No, You Are Not Just Tired

Computer-related eye fatigue, also referred to as digital eye strain, computer vision syndrome, screen-fatigue, ocular fatigue, and asthenopia, refers to a group of eye and vision-related problems associated with prolonged staring at a digital screen, most often a computer, tablet, or cell phone. More specifically, it is what results when the visual demands of a task exceed our abilities to perform them comfortably. Research has shown that individuals who spend two or more continuous hours looking at a digital screen per day, every day are most at risk. We are looking at you, 21st-century lawyer.

What You Are Feeling Are Real Symptoms

Common symptoms of these eye problems include burning, sore, or tired eyes, sensitivity to light, vertigo, headaches, blurred/double vision, dry/watery eyes, redness, and neck and shoulder pain. According to the American Academy of Ophthalmology, individuals also experience reflex symptoms such as migraine, nausea, and twitching of facial muscles. Poor lighting, glare on a digital screen, unhealthy viewing distance, and poor seating posture usually exacerbate the severity of these symptoms.[40:1]

Our Eyes Are Not Adapted To Digital Screens

It all boils down to the incompatibility between how our eyes have evolved to work and the physical demands of focusing for long periods on digital screens. Upon viewing something close-up, the muscles inside the eye contract to shape the lens, helping you focus. Looking at a digital screen for extended periods requires frequent eye movement, focusing, and alignment. Images on a digital screen are formed by tiny dots called pixels, so our eyes must work even harder to keep the pixelated images in focus than they do when reading a printed page. Hours of looking at a screen translates to hours of significant eye exertion. Our eye muscles tire and begin to hurt, resulting in the symptoms above.

SCREEN ADDICTION AND TECH DEPENDENCE

The impact of digital screens goes beyond physical concerns. Screen addiction is predicted to be the biggest non-drug addiction of the 21st century. Past concerns about our digital screens focused on how technology detracts from our interpersonal relationships. While still relevant, more recent concerns warn about our psychological dependence on them.

Research has found that we use digital screens as a coping mechanism to avoid feelings of discomfort. For some, a screen provides an escape from an uncomfortable social situation, sometimes becoming one of few, if not the only comfortable social situation. For others, the perceived need to be constantly responsive through our digital devices results in symptoms of anxiety when our access is restricted.

Over the years, many of the lawyers we have worked with exhibit attachment symptoms to their devices, including the urge to sleep with a device and irrational reactions when its use is restricted. This fear of being without your phone has become so prevalent that it has been coined as "nomophobia," short for "No Mobile Phobia." According to the *Journal of Family Medicine and Primary Care*, nomophobia is used to describe a "psychological condition when people have a fear of being detached from mobile phone connectivity."[40:2] Not limited to the physical device itself, many lawyers even demonstrate significant levels of anxiety when just asked not to check their email for a limited window of time.

While "nomophobia" is not yet in the American Psychiatric Associations *Diagnostic and Statistical Manual of Mental Disorders (DSM-V)*, experts have proposed to include it in the next edition as a specific phobia. Its legitimacy as a clinical diagnosis is further supported by psychometric scales such as "The Test of Mobile Phone Dependence" and the "Questionnaire of Dependence on Mobile Phones," which already exist as diagnostic tools.

CONSEQUENCES OF SCREEN ADDICTION AND TECH DEPENDENCE

Regardless of whether screen dependence is a diagnosable condition, the impact of our reliance on digital screens is significant. When we are always anticipating something that we need to respond to immediately, we do not have the opportunity just to be. Our devices create a waiting game environment in which we are left without much control. For many lawyers we have worked with, this waiting game often results in:

- Feeling anxious when you do not have your phone in your physical possession.
- Checking your phone for new texts, emails, messages and feeling compelled to reply immediately.
- Sensing a phantom phone vibration when the phone has not notified you of an incoming message.

The constant anticipation of technological interaction, whether that be a phone call, text, email, etc., keeps our bodies in a state of fight-or-flight, and this results in significant consequences to our cognitive capabilities (i.e., decrease in focus, increase in irritability, decrease in productivity, impaired critical thinking, etc.). See *Lesson 19: Identify Your Invisible Saber-Toothed Tigers*.

INCORPORATE SCREEN FASTS INTO YOUR DAILY ROUTINE

It's important to make screen fasts part of how you work and live. Start small with mini screen fasts. Baby steps are essential. Here are a few examples:

- Turn off your mobile notifications and place your cell phone across the room while working.
- Don't take your device into the bathroom. This also serves the added benefit of preventing phone death by sink or toilette.
- Keep your phone out of bed. Checking your email, the news, or social media as part of your sleep routine may feel like a final effort at productivity or a comforting distraction but staring at your device during this period in your circadian rhythm negatively impacts your brains' ability to set you up for restful sleep.
- Turn off your phone completely while you are sleeping. You do not and should not be checking for messages during a 4:00 a.m. bathroom break. It's not good for your sleep or your work product.
- Next, move on to:
    - » Don't check your device first thing in the morning. Wait to check your phone until after a specific part of your morning routine (i.e., after changing clothes, brushing your teeth, or eating breakfast).
    - » Set aside a focus time for the tasks which require the most focus—for lawyers, this is often research and writing. During this focus time, turn off your email and all messaging apps and put that phone beyond arm's length.
    - » Eat meals without looking at a screen.
- It will feel like you are setting yourself up to miss something important, but keep in mind that you are more likely to receive a phone call if there is an emergency in the day and that emails and messages requiring replies can wait 45 – 60 minutes.

LIVING THE LESSON

- Start with mini screen fasts. As you practice shorter periods without your phone at hand, you are progressively rewiring your brain to be okay without it.

- Once mini screen fasts are part of your daily routine, incorporate periodic screen fasts into your work.
- Use your vacation as a time to test out an extended periodic screen fast. For example, let your team know that you will only be checking your device during specific time slots each day and that they will need to call you if there is an emergency outside of those time slots.
- Pick one day per month (or per week if you are really going for it) to not check your devices.
- As you are working on building up your psychological screen fast muscles, minimize the physical impact of your screens by incorporating best practices for looking at them. For example:
- Apply the 20-20-20 rule. For every 20 minutes looking at a screen, take a 20-second break and look at something 20 feet away.
  1. Set a timer for every 20 minutes. See *Lesson 30: Make Friends with a Timer.*
  2. When the 20-minute timer goes off, set another timer for 20 seconds and stand up, stretch, and look at something 20 feet away. At the end of those 20 seconds, reset the 20-minute timer and continue with your task.
- Incorporate *eye yoga* into your workday.
  1. Look to the left, hold the position, and then look to the right, hold the position.
  2. Look up, hold the position, and then look down, hold the position.
  3. Repeat four times, closing your eyes and taking a breath in between.
- Increase the font size on your screen, so you don't need to squint.
- Use a monitor screen (also available for phones and tablets) to reduce monitor glare and blue-light exposure.
- Sit at least 25 inches from your screen.
- If you use your laptop, tablet, or phone to watch videos, watch on a TV instead. A large screen at a greater distance is better for your eyes than a small one that is close.

[40:1] Koushik Tripathy, "Computer Vision Syndrome (Digital Eye Strain)" *American Academy of Ophthalmology* (March 17, 2022).
https://eyewiki.org/Computer_Vision_Syndrome_(Digital_Eye_Strain)#Symptoms.5B2.5D.5B4.5D
[40:2] Sudip Bhattacharya, Md Abu Bashar, Abhay Srivastava, and Amarjeet Singh, "*NOMOPHOBIA: NO MObile PHone PHOBIA.*" *Journal of Family Medicine and Primary Care*, April 2019, 8(4): 1297–1300. https://www.ncbi.nlm.nih.gov/pmc/articles/PMC6510111/

ADDITIONAL RESOURCES

- American Optometric Association, "20-20-20 Rule cheat sheet" *AOA* (2022). https://www.aoa.org/AOA/Images/Patients/Eye%20Conditions/20-20-20-rule.pdf

Lesson 41

EMPATHY IS ABOUT HAPPINESS, TOO.

Could a greater miracle take place than for us to look through each other's eyes for an instant?

– HENRY DAVID THOREAU

When you think about empathy, what do you think of? For many people, being empathic means sharing another person's sorrows, feeling another person's pain, and walking in their shoes. As we said in *Lesson 34: Listen with Empathy*, being empathic means feeling sorrow "*with* someone, not just *for* them." When we express that kind of empathy, we are bringing more happiness to the other person's life and to our own as well.

Empathy for another's pain or distress is what we typically think of when we think of empathy. But researchers have found that humans also have the capacity to empathize with another person's happiness and joy.[41:1] In addition, researchers have found that being empathic (or becoming more empathic) is something we can learn, much like resilience and other characteristics that contribute to our happiness and well-being. While some of us may be more genetically predisposed to feeling and showing empathy, we can all develop our empathic abilities. This takes time, desire, and effort, but like so much of what is meaningful in life, it's worth it.

Researchers have also distinguished three different types of empathy. In an article for *Psychology Today*, Dona Matthews briefly describes each type:[41:2]

- **Cognitive Empathy**
  This is often referred to as perspective-taking and involves the ability to see and identify with other people's emotions.

- **Emotional Empathy**
  This type of empathy is the emotional contagion we refer to in *Lesson 21: Make Someone Happy.*
- **Compassionate Empathy**
  This is also called empathic concern and is demonstrated by a desire to care for others, feel their feelings, and want to help.

We know this may sound like a lot of psychological mumbo jumbo, but stick with us here. Or rather, stick with Dr. Mathews because she concisely describes each of these types of empathy.

> *Each of these forms of empathy is useful and appropriate in the right circumstance but problematic when misapplied. I once received a helpful piece of advice about the limits of empathy: When someone has fallen into an emotional well, they don't want you climbing down into the well with them (emotional empathy). They'd much rather you see and understand the problem they're experiencing (cognitive empathy) and throw them down a rope (compassionate empathy).*
>
> – From *"Empathy: Were Kindness, Compassion, and Happiness Begin"*

Think of your work as a lawyer. You are often sitting across the desk from someone who has "fallen into an emotional well." It doesn't matter if they are a sophisticated business owner who has been a party to litigation before or a mom with terminal cancer planning the end of her life. Emotional wells are everywhere. You're likely already applying all three types of empathy in your practice, even if you weren't aware of it until now.

So, back to empathy and happiness. Empathy brings many benefits that are good for us and, taken together, work to support our overall happiness. In his book, *Empathy: Why It Matters and How to Get It,*[41:3] Roman Krznaric notes that empathy has the power to heal broken relationships. It can deepen our friendships and help us to create new ones. Empathy can also enhance our creative thinking because it broadens our perspectives. Krznaric advocates for a revolution of empathy in which we can truly share in both the sorrows and joys of others to bring more happiness and well-being to their lives and our own.

> *The idea of collective empathy is especially relevant today because it counterbalances the highly individualistic focus of modern self-help culture,*

which tends to view the search for happiness or well-being as a personal pursuit concerning our own ambitions and desires, rather than one that involves working with others toward common goals. Yet thinkers going back to Aristotle have recognized that we are social animals and that joy and meaning in life grow, in good part, from being immersed in something larger than ourselves. Human beings thrive on "we" as much as "me."

– From *Empathy: Why It Matters and How to Get It*

HOW TO BUILD YOUR EMPATHY SKILLS

As we mentioned above, neuroscientists agree that our capacity for empathy is influenced by our genetics. It's also a skill that can be developed. In a 2021 article for *We Humans*,[41:4] Stanford psychology professor Jamil Zaki, author of *The War for Kindness*,[41:5] suggests five exercises that you can use to build your empathy:

1. Strengthen your internal resources by practicing self-compassion.
2. Spend kindness on others. See *Lesson 24: Get High—A Helper's High, That is.*
3. Disagree without debating. This one is a challenge for many of us, but according to Zaki, worth doing.
4. Use technology to connect, not just to click and comment.
5. Praise empathy in others. If you see empathy in someone else, acknowledge them for it.

LIVING THE LESSON

- Experiment with Dr. Zaki's five exercises. Observe how you feel.
- Do your best to really feel the happiness of others when they share it with you. If it's appropriate, give them a hug.
- Show interest in the happy circumstances of others. Ask them to tell you more about the experience. It can boost their happiness and yours.
- Share your joy and happy experiences with others so that they can revel in your happiness.

[41:1] Carrie Steckl, "Empathy: It's About Happiness, Too" *American Addiction Centers*. https://www.mentalhelp.net/blogs/empathy-it-s-about-happiness-too/
[41:2] Dona Matthews, "Empathy: Where Kindness, Compassion, and Happiness Begin." *Psychology Today* (October 31. 2019).
https://www.psychologytoday.com/us/blog/going-beyond-intelligence/201910/empathy-where-kindness-compassion-and-happiness-begin
[41:3] Roman Krznaric, *Empathy: Why It Matters and How to Get It* (Penguin Group, 2014).
[41:4] Thu-Huong Ha, "5 Exercises to Help You Build more Empathy." *We Humans* (March 16, 2021).
https://ideas.ted.com/5-exercises-to-help-you-build-more-empathy/
[41:5] Jamil Zaki, *The War for Kindness: Building Empathy in a Fractured World* (Broadway Books, 2019).

ADDITIONAL RESOURCES

- Roman Krznaric, "Six Habits of Highly Empathic People." *Greater Good Magazine* (November 27, 2012).
- https://greatergood.berkeley.edu/article/item six_habits_of_highly_empathic_people1

Lesson 42

MAKE YOUR BED.

If you want to change the world, start off by making your bed.

– William H. McRaven

Do you make your bed in the morning? When you were a kid, maybe your parents instilled the importance of making your bed each morning. Or maybe they didn't. If they did, it might still be a daily habit for you. Or maybe you ditched it as soon as you got your own place.

Some people can't begin their day without making the bed. Others, not so much. If you're in the "not so much" category, you might want to reconsider. Stacking up small wins throughout the day—like making your bed—can make you more organized, focused, and happier. Although we're not sure who said, "The state of your bed is the state of your head," there is some science behind it.

According to the research, the benefits of making your bed in the morning are many. Over the past couple of decades, various studies have found that people who make their beds are typically happier and more productive than those who don't. A study reported in *Psychology Today* found that "71% of bed makers consider themselves happy, while 62% of non-bed-makers admit to being unhappy. Bed makers are also more likely to like their jobs, own a home, exercise regularly, and feel well-rested, whereas non-bed-makers hate their jobs, rent apartments, avoid the gym, and wake up tired. All in all, bed makers are happier and more successful than their rumple-sheeted peers." [42:1]

Another benefit of making your bed—although it may seem silly to some—is that it gives you a sense of accomplishment first thing in the morning, and it can prepare you for other things you may not want to do later in the day. Retired Navy four-star admiral William H. McRaven wrote about the value of bed making in the aptly titled book *Make Your Bed: Little Things That Can Change Your Life . . . and Maybe the World.*[42:2] While McRaven doesn't speak about the idea that making your bed each morning can make you feel happier, he does emphasize that the seemingly little things we do each day can make a big difference in our lives.

> *If you make your bed every morning, you will have accomplished the first task of the day. It will give you a small sense of pride, and it will encourage you to do another task and another and another. By the end of the day, that one task completed will have turned into many tasks completed. Making your bed will also reinforce the fact that little things in life matter.*
>
> – From *Make Your Bed: Little Things That Can Change Your Life . . . and Maybe the World*

In his book, *The Power of Habit: Why We Do What We Do in Life and Business,* author Charles Duhigg considers making your bed each day a "keystone habit." According to Duhigg, some habits matter more than others, and making your bed is one of them. Keystone habits can start "chain reactions that help other good habits take hold."[42:3] As we've noted throughout this book, lasting positive changes in our lives and our level of happiness can come from seemingly minor changes to our everyday routines. Making your bed each morning is one of those small changes that can have a lasting effect.

> *Making your bed every morning is correlated with better productivity, a greater sense of well-being, and stronger skills at sticking with a budget. It's not that a family meal or a tidy bed causes better grades or less frivolous spending. But somehow, those initial shifts start chain reactions that help other good habits take hold.*
>
> – From *The Power of Habit: Why We Do What We Do in Life and Business*

We hear what you're saying to yourself, "I don't have time to make my bed in the morning. I've got way too much to do, and I simply do not have time." If this is you, we have a challenge. Time yourself and see how long it takes you to make your bed. It will probably take you less than two minutes. Are two minutes too much time to spend on an activity that can pay big dividends on your health and happiness as the years go by?

And here's one more reason to make your bed. It's a great way to get yourself moving in the morning! You bend. You stretch. You lift. You get a couple minutes of exercise, and you set yourself up for a great day. See *Lesson 7: Start Your Day with a Good Stretch and Some Endorphins.*

LIVING THE LESSON

- Make your bed.
- Repeat every day—even on the weekends—for four weeks.
- If you like the way it makes you feel, then continue.
- If not, simply return to your rumpled sheet life. It's okay. Do what makes you happy.

[42:1] Judy Dutton, "Make Your Bed, Change Your Life?" *Psychology Today* (August 16, 2012). https://www.psychologytoday.com/us/blog/brain-candy/201208/make-your-bed-change-your-life
[42:2] William McRaven, *Make Your Bed: Little Things That Can Change Your Life . . . and Maybe the World* (Grand Central Publishing, 2017).
[42:3] Duhigg, Charles, *The Power of Habit: Why We Do What We Do in Life and Business* (Random House Trade Paperbacks, 2014).

Lesson 43

LET IT GO.

It's funny how some distance makes everything seem small
And the fears that once controlled me can't get to me at all
It's time to see what I can do
To test the limits and break through
No right, no wrong, no rules for me
I'm free

– *"Let It Go" from Frozen*

If you have kids, and even if you don't, you probably know the song "Let It Go" from the Disney musical *Frozen*. In the musical, Elsa sings about not caring what people think and gives us all words to live by, "The past is in the past. Let it go." Elsa had it right.

Letting go sounds so simple, but our brains can sometimes make what sounds simple quite challenging. Neuroscience has shown that our brains process positive and negative information differently.[43:1] It requires more thinking to process negative experiences than it does to process positive experiences. Consequently, we can get really good at remembering the negative events in our lives. We play them over and over in our minds. Gustavo Razzetti, who writes "The Adaptive Mind" blog for *Psychology Today*, says it so well, "Reliving sad memories makes us feel like a hamster in the wheel—no matter how hard we try, we can't move forward."[43:2]

Psychology refers to reliving sad memories as rumination. Whether we want to or not, sometimes our brains will ruminate. It can be torture to relive memories that we would rather forget. But by understanding how our brains work, we can begin to break the cycle. Once we understand how our brains work, we can train ourselves to get off the hamster wheel.

If you let go a little, you will have a little happiness.
If you let go a lot, you will have a lot of happiness.
If you let go completely, you will be free.
– AJAHN CHAH

While letting go can certainly encompass letting go of the past, it can also be applied to many other situations in our life. In *Just One Thing*,[43:3] Rick Hanson explains the importance of letting go of more than just the past.

> *Letting go can mean several things: releasing pain; dropping thoughts, words, and deeds that cause suffering and harm; yielding rather than breaking; surrendering to the way it is, like it or not; allowing each moment to pass away without trying to hold on to it; accepting the permanently impermanent nature of existence; and relaxing the sense of self and opening out into the wider world.*
>
> – FROM *JUST ONE THING*

Regardless of whether you are letting go of the past or letting go of something else, your brain is going to need some training. Thankfully, you can use your mind to train your brain. See *Lesson 8: The One Thing That Can Change Everything*. According to Hanson, letting go takes strength, fortitude, character, and insight. And when we summon these qualities to help us let go, we become supple and resilient, like a willow tree in a storm. We are able to flow through life without being held down or held back by things that no longer serve us.

HOW TO LET GO

In *Just One Thing*, Hanson gives examples of different types of letting go. He reminds us to notice how often we let go of things throughout the day. We let go of objects; we move from one feeling to another; we say goodbye; we change the TV channel; we throw out the trash. These are all forms of letting go that we rarely think about. Letting go is okay. In fact, sometimes it's necessary and beneficial to our well-being and happiness.

Letting go may not be easy at first. But, as with so many things in life, the more you practice letting go, the easier it will become. Here are a few examples of how to let go from *Just One Thing*:

- Let go of tension in your body. Take long, slow breaths to engage your parasympathetic nervous system, which helps you relax.
- Let go of things you no longer use or need. Give them away to someone who can use them. Notice how great it feels to have more space in your closet or garage.
- Pick a grievance, grudge, or resentment and commit to moving on. Forgiving others doesn't mean that you're okay with what they have done. It means you have resolved not to let it upset you any longer.

Let good things come into the space that's been opened up by whatever you've let go.
These could be more time, freedom, energy, peace, creativity, or love.
– *Rick Hanson*

When you let go of something that happened in the past or the emotion you are experiencing in the moment, it can feel amorphous. In an article, Hanson wrote for *Greater Good Magazine*,[43:4] he gives advice on how to make the act of letting go more tangible.

> *You can help yourself let something go by making it concrete. For example, put a small stone or other object in your hand and imagine that it is the thing you've been attached to. Hold onto it hard; let your desires and thoughts about it flow through awareness; feel the costs related to it; and when you're ready, open your hand and drop it—and open as well to any sense of relief, freedom, ease, or insight. You could do a similar practice by writing a note about this attachment, and then tearing it up and letting its pieces fall away. Or you could talk with a trusted being—perhaps a friend or therapist, or in your own kind of prayer—and explore the attachment, communicate your intentions to move on, and let it go.*

LIVING THE LESSON

- Notice how often you let go of things throughout the day. Make a conscious choice to acknowledge that it is okay to let go.

- Notice when you are holding on to a painful experience in the past. Let it go.
- Remind yourself we can't learn or grow or change without letting go.

[43:1] Alina Tugend, "Praise is Fleeting, but Brickbats We Recall." New York Times (March 23, 2012). https://www.nytimes.com/2012/03/24/your-money/why-people-remember-negative-events-more-than-positive-ones.html
[43:2] Gustavo Razzetti, "How to Let Go of the Past." Psychology Today (February 13, 2020). https://www.psychologytoday.com/us/blog/the-adaptive-mind/202002/how-let-go-the-past
[43:3] Rick Hanson, Just One Thing: Developing a Buddha Brain One Simple Practice at a Time (New Harbinger Publications, 2011).
[43:4] Rick Hanson, "Just One Thing: Let It Go." Greater Good Magazine (January 5, 2015). https://greatergood.berkeley.edu/article/item/just_one_thing_let_it_go

Lesson 44

PROTECT YOURSELF AGAINST COMPASSION FATIGUE.

There is a cost to caring.

– Charles R. Figley

If you think about why you became a lawyer, more than one answer may come up for you. Maybe you have wanted to be a lawyer since you were a child. We know many lawyers for whom this is true. Maybe your mom or dad was a lawyer, and they influenced you. Perhaps you were intrigued and fascinated by the law, or you saw the legal profession as a solid career that could open other doors for you. Whatever your reason (or reasons), we are pretty sure that helping others was part of your decision. There are plenty of negative lawyer jokes out there. But the truth is, lawyers care. And sometimes, lawyers care too much.

WHAT IS COMPASSION FATIGUE?

In *Lesson 4*, we talked about the symptoms of burnout. Like burnout, compassion fatigue is a human response to overwhelming stress. The symptoms of burnout and compassion fatigue are similar. Some symptoms of both conditions include emotional exhaustion, excessive worry, negative thoughts, sleep disturbance, disorganization, and a feeling of helplessness. While they are similar in their symptoms and how to protect yourself against them, there is an important distinction between the two. Burnout is the result of work-related pressure and stress. Compassion fatigue results from the cumulative effect of exposure to traumatic stories or events. And although "the symptoms are similar, compassion fatigue results over a shorter period of time due to the intensity of the suffering."[44:1]

In an article for the North Carolina Lawyer Assistance Program, Beth Hudnall Stamm described compassion fatigue as our brain's neurological response to continual exposure to trauma. For lawyers, this is your clients' trauma. You hear their stories every day. You live with their stories. You often take their stories home with you at night. "Unfortunately, all the best legal training in the world cannot turn off our mirror neurons, that highly-evolved part of our brain which responds neurologically-emotionally to other people's distress as an involuntary response (even when we might not have any conscious awareness of an emotional response)."[44:2]

> *There is a cost to caring. Professionals who listen to clients' stories of fear, pain, and suffering may feel similar fear, pain, and suffering because they care. Sometimes we feel we are losing our sense of self to the clients we serve ... Those who have an enormous capacity for feeling and expressing empathy tend to be more at risk of compassion stress.*
>
> – From *Compassion Fatigue: Coping with Secondary Traumatic Stress Disorder in Those Who Treat the Traumatized*[44:3]

Stamm notes that judges are at greater risk of developing compassion fatigue because they are exposed day after day to the traumatic stories from the parties before them. In addition to judges, attorneys in the practice areas below face a heightened risk of compassion fatigue because of the issues involved in their clients' cases:

- Criminal Law
- Family Law
- Personal Injury and Workers' Compensation Law
- Medical Malpractice Law
- Personal Bankruptcy
- Wills, Trusts, and Estates

WHAT YOU CAN DO TO PROTECT YOURSELF AGAINST COMPASSION FATIGUE

Most of the lessons in this book can help you protect yourself against compassion fatigue. But the first step is awareness.

> *The reality is that lawyers are human beings. Any person, regardless of professional competence, can develop compassion fatigue. The struggle*

for lawyers is the assumption (both their own and that of others) that they will not be impacted by the work that they do. The reality can be quite different. Lawyers that are exposed to traumatic stories and events may have physiological reactions such as increased heart rate, breathing rate, and muscle tension. They can have emotional responses such as sadness, anger, or fear. They may also experience changes in their assumptions about life, other people, and issues of safety.

– From "Keeping Legal Minds Intact: Mitigating Compassion Fatigue" [44:4]

Awareness is key to being able to protect yourself from and mitigate compassion fatigue. Pay attention to how you are feeling. Recognize the signs of compassion fatigue and take action. One of the best articles we've seen on compassion fatigue in the legal profession is from the Missouri Bar. [44:5] Although its focus is on judges, the suggestions on responses to compassion fatigue are relevant to all lawyers. Below are just some of the research-based strategies suggested in the article, together with references to relevant lessons in this book:

- Recognize the situation and the signs that led to it.
- Find resilience. See *Lesson 3: Why Resilience Matters.*
- Start with the basics: enough good sleep, fitness, and eating well. See *Lesson 17: Get Enough Sleep* and *Lesson 36: Get Your Butt Up and Out of That Chair.*
- Think about:
    - What do you really enjoy? See *Lesson 32: Do What You Used to Do – Play.*
    - What gives you meaning in your work and personal life? See *Lesson 5: Get Clear on Your Why.*
    - What will help you recharge? See *Lesson 39: Recovery is Essential for an Athlete's Performance. Yours, Too.*
    - Focus on those items.
    - Plan to do them soon.
- Embrace your sense of humor. See *Lesson 20: Have a Good Laugh.*
- Seek support.
    - Spend regular time with family and friends. See *Lesson 31: Cultivate Positive, Supportive Friendships.*
    - Participate in creative non-work activities. See *Lesson 32: Do What You Used to Do – Play.*

- Turn to your hobbies.
- Take time away. See *Lesson 39: Recovery is Essential for an Athlete's Performance. Yours, Too.*
- Vacations are important.
    - Take one or plan one soon.
    - Take mini-breaks and regular vacations.
    - Small mental breaks—see a play, a movie, a concert, or your favorite sport.

LIVING THE LESSON

- Understand that you are a human being. Your response to the trauma of others is not different because you are a lawyer.
- Work to increase your self-awareness.
- Familiarize yourself with the symptoms of compassion fatigue, and take action if you notice them.

[44:1] Gray Robinson, "Preventing Compassion Fatigue: When Lawyers Care Too Much." *Attorney at Work* (August 12, 2021).
https://www.attorneyatwork.com/preventing-compassion-fatigue/
[44:2] Beth Hudnall Stamm, "Compassion Fatigue." *North Carolina Lawyer Assistance Program.* https://www.nclap.org/compassion-fatigue/
[44:3] Charles R. Figley, *Compassion Fatigue: Coping with Secondary Traumatic Stress Disorder in Those Who Treat the Traumatized* (Charles R. Figley ed., 1995).
[44:4] Linda Albert, "Keeping Legal Minds Intact: Mitigating Compassion Fatigue." *Wisconsin Lawyers Assistance Program* (April 24, 2015).
https://wisatj.org/avoiding-compassion-fatigue
[44:5] Anne Chambers, "Judges and Compassion Fatigue: What Is It and What to Do About It" *The Missouri Bar.*
https://mobar.org/site/content/Articles/Well_Being/Judges_and_Compassion_Fatigue__What_Is_It_and_What_to_Do_About_It.aspx

Lesson 45

REKINDLE YOUR FRIENDSHIP WITH PEN AND PAPER.

I can shake off everything as I write; my sorrows disappear; my courage is reborn.

– Anne Frank

If you're a digital native, someone who has integrated technology into nearly every aspect of your life, you are not alone. Typing on a device has become the default mode of writing for most professionals. For those of us who came of age in the time of analog, we have spent more time during the past twenty years writing on a screen than on a piece of paper. If you've been typing on a keyboard for as long you can remember, you might want to consider getting back to basics—at least some of the time. Typing offers the obvious benefit of efficiency yet lacks the benefits of the mind-body connection we get from writing with pen (or pencil) and paper.

HANDWRITING IS A NEUROSENSORY EXPERIENCE

Handwriting is a complex task that requires several simultaneous skills such as holding the pen, feeling the paper, moving the writing implement, and directing it with your thoughts. Each letter requires a unique set of movements. In contrast, typing on a keyboard only requires you to press a key with little to no distinction between movements because you press a key in the same way for every letter. As a result of the higher level of engagement, handwriting stimulates the brain significantly.[45:1]

In a large study of university students, researchers found that those who handwrote their class notes were better equipped to answer questions on a lecture than those who typed their notes. The study, reported in *The Journalist's Resource*, found that in contrast with the near-verbatim notes of those who typed, the process of handwriting required the other students to rephrase the information from the lecture in a way that they understood. Students who handwrote their notes simultaneously engaged in summarizing and comprehension, aiding their understanding of the material.[45:2] Maybe there is something to be said for taking notes—the old-fashioned way—with a pen and a legal pad.

This study confirmed the findings of earlier research on children and adults that found individuals who learned to write letters by hand were better at recognizing letters than those who learned them on a keyboard. Like the university students, handwriting required these research subjects to engage in multiple ways with the writing process, including developing muscle memory by repeating tasks over and over again.[45:3] This allows us to perform those tasks with decreasing effort. So, if you're thinking, I really don't like writing by hand, try experimenting with it. It's a great exercise for your brain, and it will get easier the more you do it.

HANDWRITING IMPROVES MEMORY

As we record information by hand, our brains create spatial relationships between data points. Handwriting activates the parts of the brain involved in memory and thinking. Each unique movement helps encode the information in the brain, improving our ability to store and recall that information. Here's another reason why taking notes by hand improves our memory. In an interview with *The Huffington Post Australia*, Helen Macpherson from the Institute for Physical Activity and Nutrition (IPAN) at Deakin University explained, "When we write by hand, we have to coordinate verbal and fine movement systems. And when we learn new information, for example, at school or in a university lecture, we don't write verbatim, which means we have to create our own summaries and concepts. Basically, because we can keep pace typing, but we can't keep pace with handwriting, it means we have different ways of encoding the information, which in turn leads to richer memory."[45:4]

HANDWRITING IMPROVES CRITICAL THINKING

When we write by hand, we think more thoroughly about the information we are recording because we need to process and translate it into a format we understand. This format can be unique to each individual and requires that many factors be considered: diction, syntax, size, shape, format, etc. We make more connections with the information being recorded when handwriting than when typing because there are more elements required to complete the task.

HANDWRITING IMPROVES COMPREHENSION

Like the benefits of memory and critical thinking, the improved comprehension connected to handwriting also results from the increased brain activity required. Researchers also theorize that the typically slower nature of handwriting, in contrast with typing, results in an inability to record information verbatim, requiring us to think about what we are writing.

LIVING THE LESSON

- Experiment with using pen and paper for the following projects:
    - » Your to-do and to-don't lists. See *Lesson 27: Make a To-Don't List.*
    - » Your gratitude journal. See *Lesson 11: Create a Mindset of Gratitude.*
    - » Your Values Exercise. See *Lesson 5: Get Clear on Your Why.*
- Take handwritten notes when learning something new, even if you save them digitally later.
- Prepare for a difficult conversation by handwriting your talking points.
- Give yourself a pep talk in writing. Remember, the more you write by hand, the easier it gets.

[45:1] Anne Chemin, "Handwriting vs Typing: Is the Pen Still Mightier Than the Keyboard?" *The Guardian* (December 14, 2016).
https://www.theguardian.com/science/2014/dec/16/cognitive-benefits-handwriting-decline-typing
[45:2] Joanna Penn, "The Pen is Mightier Than the Keyboard: Advantages of Longhand Over Laptop Note Taking." *The Journalist's Resource* (July 30, 2014).
https://journalistsresource.org/education/longhand-versus-laptop-note-taking/
[45:3] Marieke Longcamp, Marie-Therese Zerbato-Poudou, and Jean-Luc Velay, "The influence of writing practice on letter recognition in preschool children: a comparison between handwriting and typing." *National Library of Medicine* (January 4, 2005).
https://pubmed.ncbi.nlm.nih.gov/15823243/

[45:4] Emily Blatchford, "Writing By Hand Improves Your Memory, Experts Say." *Huffpost* (July 14, 2016). https://www.huffpost.com/entry/writing-by-hand-improves-your-memory-experts-say_n_61087608e4b0999d2084f66b

ADDITIONAL RESOURCES

- "Typing vs. Handwriting: Which Is Better for Your Memory?" (January 6, 2018).https://youtu.be/pu0PSZ_EwII

Lesson 46

TRY SOMETHING NEW.

All life is an experiment. The more experiments the better.

– Ralph Waldo Emerson

As humans, we are naturally curious. We are wired to learn, and we do so through new experiences. When we do new things, we learn new things, and learning is good for the brain. Studies have found that the density of the white matter in our brains increases when we try something new, and the more we learn, the easier it becomes to learn, and our brains work more efficiently.[46:1]

Challenging your brain activates processes that aid in maintaining brain cells and in establishing new neuropathways between them. This, in turn, helps improve memory, adaptability, and problem-solving skills. Improving these skills will have a positive impact on our sense of wellness and well-being. By trying something new from time to time, you can create a flywheel of continuous improvement in a whole host of areas that contribute to your happiness.

TRYING SOMETHING NEW CAN BOOST POSITIVITY, IMPROVE YOUR MOOD, AND HELP YOU RELAX

The greater the variety of experiences we have, the more likely we will focus on positive emotions and minimize negative ones.[46:2] By helping us focus on positive emotions, our new experiences can have a long-term effect on our lives. In *Lesson 11*, we cited research from the book *Positivity* by Barbara Fredrickson, which found "positivity doesn't simply reflect success and health, it can also produce success and health. This means that even after positivity fades, we can find traces of its impact. Beyond the present pleasant moment, your positivity has downstream consequences for the very trajectory of your life."[46:3]

The increased focus on positive emotions also directly improves mood and helps you relax. Trying something new contributes to increased relaxation because it can serve as a source of healthy and positive distraction. Finally, exposure to new stimuli distracts our brains from negative thoughts and worries, allowing us to practice being present in the moment. See *Lesson 8: The One Thing That Can Change Everything.*

DOING SOMETHING NEW CAN IMPROVE YOUR CONFIDENCE

On the surface, doing something new might seem like an invitation for insecurity. On the contrary, trying something new is more likely to improve your confidence. Even if you fail, you can feel proud for trying and consequently increase your likelihood of trying other new things in the future. Studies have found that overcoming a fear of failure builds courage and curiosity, both connected to increased levels of well-being. See *Lesson 48: Don't Be Afraid to Fail.*

If you try something new and succeed, you are likely to experience more confidence and gather evidence to combat negative thinking that may have previously limited you. Either way, trying something new offers opportunities to improve well-being.

Life begins at the end of your comfort zone.
– *Neale Donald Walsch*

IT'S OKAY IF NEW THINGS ARE UNCOMFORTABLE—THEY'RE SUPPOSED TO BE

Doing something new can be both uncomfortable and exhilarating. That's okay. On the one hand, we have evolved to do new things and enjoy learning from them. On the other hand, we have also evolved to fear the unknown. Both serve the evolutionary purpose of self-preservation. When we embrace the juxtaposed feelings of fear and joy, we give ourselves the opportunity to choose to enjoy life in new ways.

Do one thing every day that scares you.
– ELEANOR ROOSEVELT

TRYING SOMETHING NEW CAN BE BIG OR SMALL

Trying something new can be big, like going skydiving for the first time, or small, like taking a different route home. Either way, big or small, stepping out of your comfort zone can help keep your mind sharp and mood positive. Consider starting small by tweaking something you already do.

LIVING THE LESSON

- Cook a new recipe this week.
- Tweak your workout routine to include new moves.
- Try exercising outside instead of inside.
- Take a new route home.
- Read a non-fiction book for pleasure.
- Try a new activity—scuba diving, knitting, horseback riding, painting, pottery, a new language, a musical instrument, anything!
- Make a commitment to learn a new skill each year.

[46:1] Brian Wong, "How Learning a New Skill Helps Your Mind Grow Stronger." *Inc. Magazine* (December 29, 2017).
https://www.inc.com/brian-wong/how-learning-a-new-skill-helps-your-mind-grow-stronger.html
[46:1] Time Magazine Staff, "Health and Happiness: Try New Things" *Time Magazine.* http://content.time.com/time/specials/2007/article/0,28804,1631176_1630611_1630586,00.html
[46:3] Barbara Fredrickson, *Positivity: Groundbreaking Research Reveals How to Embrace the Hidden Strength of Positive Emotions, Overcome Negativity, and Thrive* (Crown Archetype, 2008).

Lesson 47

EAT DESSERT FIRST.

Life is short. Eat dessert first.

– Jacques Torres

You've probably heard that quote from Jacques Torres dozens of times. Maybe you've even said it yourself. Torres, a James Beard Award recipient, is known as Mr. Chocolate and is considered one of the finest pastry chefs in the world. His mantra above rings true for more reasons than you might imagine. It speaks to the importance of enjoying the things we love and not putting off doing what we love to do. Or perhaps it's time to rediscover what you *used to love to do*. See *Lesson 32: Do What You Used to Do—Play*. But beyond the idea of doing what we love to do and not limiting the fun in our lives, eating dessert first might be a healthy option.

According to a 2019 study by the American Psychological Association,[47:1] eating dessert first might actually be good for you, or at least not as bad as you might have thought. Here's the deal. When you eat dessert first, it may affect how much you actually consume. Eating dessert after a meal can cause us to over-indulge. Don't take our word for it. Think about it yourself. Haven't you rewarded yourself with an indulgent dessert after eating a healthy meal? The study found that if we eat dessert before the main meal, we're likely to eat less and healthier.

"If we choose something healthy first, then this gives us a license to choose something bigger later," says Martin Reimann, an assistant professor of marketing and cognitive science at the University of Arizona. "If you turn it around and choose something heavier early on, then this license is already expired."[47:2]

Beyond merely eating healthier, eating dessert first is a metaphor for life. Allow yourself to enjoy the things you love throughout your day. In *Lesson 3*, we talk about the importance of building micro-resilience. An important aspect of micro-resilience is refreshing your body throughout the day. Refreshing your body includes taking breaks, stretching, sipping water, and resting your eyes from the computer screen. Your micro-resilience breaks can also include *dessert.* Maybe your dessert is a cupcake, cappuccino, or iced matcha green tea. Whatever it is for you, give yourself permission to enjoy it—in moderation, of course.

I say no to nothing, yes to moderation. That's how I approach everything. No matter if it's candy or foie gras. When you have the real deal, you're satisfied with that one bite. I say go full throttle and call it a day.

– *Carla Hall*

LIVING THE LESSON

- Experiment with the idea of eating dessert first. How does it make you feel?
- Look for opportunities during the day to "eat dessert first."
- Are there things you love to do that you've been putting off or simply not doing? Pick one and go do it.

[47:1] David Flores, Martin Reimann, Raquel Castaño, and Alberto Lopez, "If I indulge first, I will eat less overall: The unexpected interaction effect of indulgence and presentation order on consumption." *Journal of Experimental Psychology: Applied,* 25(2), (2019): 162–176. https://psycnet.apa.org/record/2019-04355-001?doi=1

[47:2] Shahrzad Warkentin, "Want to Eat Healthier? Science Says Go Ahead & Have Dessert—First." *Tiny Beans* (March 5, 2019).

Lesson 48

DON'T BE AFRAID TO FAIL.

You may encounter many defeats, but you must not be defeated. In fact, it may be necessary to encounter the defeats, so you can know who you are, what you can rise from, how you can still come out of it.

– Maya Angelou

Failure is a part of life. You've heard it said many times before. You can't succeed if you're not willing to fail. It's not how many times you fall; it's how many times you get back up. The quotes and sayings about failure are almost cliché because they've been repeated over and over and over again. Why? Because they're true. But don't get us wrong. We're not afraid to sprinkle quotes and sayings about failure liberally throughout this lesson, even if you might think they are cliché, because we are not afraid to fail.

We are all failures—at least the best of us are.

– J.M. Barrie

For most lawyers, though, failure is scary. There are few professions in which the practitioners literally have the lives of others in their hands. There are consequences if you fail in your work as a lawyer. At the same time, you and everyone in your office will make mistakes. You will not win every case you take on, but you can learn from your mistakes and failures. In fact, learning from our mistakes and failures is how we improve—how we grow.

I've made a lot of mistakes, but I've learned from every one of them. Some of them have been really painful. Losing is no fun. Truth is—we might learn more from the cases we lose than the cases we win.

– Gregory M. Stokes, Founding Member of Stokes & Kopitsky, P.A.

Although it may seem counterintuitive, failure is an essential element of success. As a result, those who study success recommend embracing failure and learning from it—the sooner, the better. We know this is another concept that is easy to say yet difficult to do. But the only way to get better at something that is not easy to do is to do it. Take the risk. Make the mistake. Fail. Learn. Get better. Move on.

In his book, *The Pursuit of Perfect*, Tal Ben-Shahar writes, "We can only learn to deal with failure by actually experiencing failure, by living through it. The earlier we face difficulties and drawbacks, the better prepared we are to deal with the inevitable obstacles along our path."[48:1]

> *If we avoid hardships and challenges because we may fail, the message we are sending ourselves is that we are unable to deal with difficulty—in this case, unable to handle failure—and our self-esteem suffers as a result. But if we do challenge ourselves, the message we internalize is that we are resilient enough to handle potential failure.*
>
> – From *The Pursuit of Perfect*

In her book, *Feel the Fear and Do It Anyway*, Susan Jeffers defines *the fear of failure* as a fear that involves the ego. It is a fear that involves our state of mind and reflects our sense of self and ability to handle whatever the world may throw at us.[48:2] Jeffers' book provides advice and strategies to help you move out of your comfort zone and past fear, whatever the fear may be. Spoiler Alert! The title is a give-away. The only way to move past our fears is to feel the fear and do it anyway.

> *There are no failures—just experiences and your reactions to them.*
>
> – *Tom Krause*

Failure is, indeed, a part of life. It can also be foundational to our success and happiness. Failure brings with it many benefits. We'll leave you with words on this topic from J.K. Rowling's 2008 Harvard University Commencement Speech, which has been viewed on YouTube more than five million times.

> *So why do I talk about the benefits of failure? Simply because failure meant a stripping away of the inessential. I stopped pretending to myself that I was anything other than what I was, and began to direct all my energy into finishing the only work that mattered to me. Had I really succeeded at anything else, I might never have found the determination to succeed in the one arena*

> *I believed I truly belonged. I was set free, because my greatest fear had been realised, and I was still alive, and I still had a daughter whom I adored, and I had an old typewriter and a big idea. And so, rock bottom became the solid foundation on which I rebuilt my life.*[48:3]

Finally, be careful when you judge your experiences as failures. Haven't there been situations in your life where in the moment you felt that you failed, but in retrospect, you realized that it wasn't a failure at all but an experience of growth and change? See *Lesson 10: Don't Be So Judgy.*

If you try to fail, and succeed, which have you done?
– *George Carlin*

LIVING THE LESSON

- Believe the clichés. Failure is a part of life and essential to our happiness and success.
- Pick something you'd like to do but never have because you feared failure. Feel the fear and do it anyway.
- Think about a time when you took on a challenge that didn't turn out as you'd hoped. Then, ask yourself:
  - » What did I learn from it?
  - » How did I grow?
  - » What might I do differently next time?

[48:1] Tal Ben-Shahar, *The Pursuit of Perfect: How to Stop Chasing Perfection and Start Living a Richer, Happier Life* (McGraw-Hill, 2009).
[48:2] Susan Jeffers, *Feel the Fear and Do It Anyway: Dynamic Techniques for Turning Fear, Indecision, and Anger into Power, Action and Love* (Jeffers Press, 2007).
[48:3] J.K. Rowling, "The Fringe Benefits of Failure, and the Importance of Imagination." *The Harvard Gazette* (June 5, 2008).
https://news.harvard.edu/gazette/story/2008/06/text-of-j-k-rowling-speech/

ADDITIONAL RESOURCES

- If you'd like to watch J.K. Rowling's Harvard Commencement Speech, you can access it here: https://www.youtube.com/watch?v=wHGqp8lz36c

Lesson 49

ACCEPT THAT YOU ARE NOT A PURELY LOGICAL BEING.

Negative emotions like loneliness, envy, and guilt have an important role to play in a happy life; they're big, flashing signs that something needs to change.

– *Gretchen Rubin*

As lawyers, we are trained to rely on logic. So much so that many of our clients over the years have expressed worry and frustration over experiencing emotions. We've heard lawyers say, "I never let emotions influence my decisions. I focus solely on the facts at hand." They equated feeling emotions with behaving emotionally, which they saw as a weakness. But our emotions are different from our behaviors.

Viewing emotions as a weakness deprives us of the helpful information that our emotions provide. Feeling and being aware of our emotions helps us consider a deeper, more detailed picture of a situation and results in decision making that is more closely aligned with our professional and personal happiness.

DON'T FIGHT YOUR EMOTIONS

We often mistakenly assume that the absence of unpleasant emotions is what makes us healthy and in control. Ironically, it is this very assumption that gives our emotions even greater power over us, but without an avenue to resolve the suffering and conflict, they can arouse in us. Acceptance Commitment Therapy (ACT) employs a metaphor about quicksand to explain the problem with fighting emotions. When in quicksand, the more we fight, the farther we sink and the more we suffer. The same happens with feelings. The more we try to avoid our feelings, the greater the hold they have on us, and the more we may suffer as a result. Like being in quicksand, we must ignore our instinct to fight our feelings. We must lay down and relax instead. The less you struggle and the more you accept, the easier it is to pull yourself out.[49:1] This is, of course, easier said than done, but it offers us a starting point from which to work.

Fighting emotions with logic is like bringing a calculator to a knife fight.
– Josh Sundquist

OBSERVE YOUR EMOTIONS AS DATA POINTS

Of course, acceptance doesn't have to mean that we tolerate problematic or dangerous situations. Acceptance reflects an openness to the validity of our feelings as a data point to consider when decision-making.

Think of your emotions like passengers on a bus, and you are the driver. You, the bus driver, decide how and where to drive the bus. Your emotions are like passengers getting on and off the bus and wanting to go to different destinations. While you can recognize and observe each passenger as they get on and off the bus, and each passenger can influence where you go, in the end, you decide where and how to drive. You could alternatively ignore the passengers, but ignoring the passengers, like ignoring our feelings, is more likely to result in an unpleasant and potentially dangerous ride. Thinking about our emotions in this way illustrates how we can both recognize our feelings and, at the same time, not let them control our behaviors. When we are able to observe ourselves in this way, we can gain a clearer understanding of the variety of forces at play as we go through our day. The better we understand the forces, the greater our ability to mitigate potential unhelpful behavior such as procrastinating on a task or not exercising.

Understanding that being nervous, having doubts, and lacking confidence are emotions that are human is how you deal with it. It is okay to feel that way ...and then understanding that you can work through it.
– Venus Williams

THE WISE MIND

On the surface, the passengers on the bus metaphor may seem like it illustrates a battle between logic and emotions. On the contrary, it demonstrates how we can observe and accept our emotions and use them in conjunction with logic to make helpful decisions using what psychology refers to as "The Wise Mind."

The Wise Mind is where reason and emotion overlap. It is the synthesis of both emotions and rational thought. It enables us to see a fuller picture of the elements at play, both the emotional and the logical. For example, you may logically know how to complete a task but find yourself struggling to do it. If there is no external, logistical, resource, or knowledge-based barrier, then it is safe to assume that there is an emotional one. You can then work to identify the emotion and use it as a data point. If we fight or ignore the emotion, then that emotion will continue to serve as a barrier. If we can acknowledge the emotion and use it as a data point along with logic, then it can help us move forward and make better decisions.

LIVING THE LESSON

- Envision the bus metaphor and make a list with pen and paper of the emotions that may be at play when you are struggling to act logically. See *Lesson 45: Rekindle your Friendship with Pen and Paper.*
- Set a reminder to do an emotion check-in three times per day. When the reminder goes off, spend two minutes writing out the emotions you have felt since your last check-in, taking into consideration how those emotions played a role in your thinking and behaviors.
- Connect with your observant self. Set a timer for two minutes and write out how a compassionate narrator would observe your experience, including emotion and reason. See *Lesson 30: Make Friends with a Timer.*

[49:1] Steven Hayes, *Get out of Your Mind and Into Your Life* (New Harbinger Publications, 2005).

ADDITIONAL RESOURCES

- "Dialectical Behavioral Therapy (DBT) Skills: Wise Mind, Emotional Mind & Reasonable Mind" (September 21, 2020). https://youtu.be/MLnUvxg_9po
- Jill Stoddard and Niloofar Afari, *The Big Book of ACT Metaphors* (New Harbinger Publications, 2014).
- "Quicksand ACT Metaphor" (October 15, 2015). https://www.youtube.com/watch?v=7DGupVaIwEY
- "Passengers on a Bus ACT Metaphor" (February 12, 2013). https://www.youtube.com/watch?v=Z29ptSuoWRc

Lesson 50

GIVE YOURSELF PERMISSION.

You are both a work in progress and a masterpiece.

– *Robin Arzon*

Here we are at the end, which is really the beginning. Now it's your time to act. If you haven't done it already, now is the time to give yourself permission to start living the lessons in this book. The word permission typically refers to someone else giving *their consent* to allow you to do something. You don't need anyone's consent or permission to live these lessons. All you need to do is give yourself permission. Yes, give yourself permission. It sounds so simple, but as we have said throughout this book, simple doesn't mean easy.

Easy or difficult, you have the power to take action. You have the power to begin—right now—to start experimenting with the lessons in this book. Psychologists use the term *agency* to describe a person's understanding that they have control over their motives, behaviors, and actions. You control your level of agency. You control your life. You can give yourself permission to be happy. No one else can do this for you.

Believe that you deserve to be happy. Even if you don't fully believe it, give yourself permission to take action as if you believed it completely. Know—deep down—that you deserve to be happy. You deserve to be happy.

Action is the foundational key to all success.

– *Pablo Picasso*

If you reflect on the lessons in this book, you'll see that each one is asking you to give yourself permission. That is what the Living the Lesson sections are all about. You can't begin to experiment with the lessons until you allow yourself to! Our message to you in this lesson is not just to read this book, but rather to give yourself permission to *live* this book—one small step at a time. Yes, you can!

Each of the 50 lessons has provided strategies you can experiment with to increase your happiness. Maybe you've tried some of these strategies before. Maybe they have worked for you, or maybe they haven't. It doesn't matter. Just because you've done something in the past and it hasn't worked doesn't mean it won't work next time. Keep at it—one step at a time. You are worth it.

Give yourself permission to be happy. It doesn't matter what's going on around you, what matters is what's going on inside you.

– Hal Elrod

Far too often, we worry about whether we are enough. We worry whether we are enough for our family, our clients, the people we work with, our community. We worry whether we are smart enough, thin enough, cool enough. We worry whether we have enough money, enough success, enough time. Give yourself permission to let go of worry. It doesn't serve you. It is useless.

Worry never robs tomorrow of its sorrow, it only saps today of its joy.

– Leo F. Buscaglia

Finally, think of permission as a gift you give yourself. But don't let it be the only gift you give yourself. As you give yourself permission to live the lessons in this book, remember to give yourself the gifts of curiosity, kindness, compassion, and grace along the way.

You can't go back and change the beginning, but you can start where you are and change the ending.

– C.S. Lewis

LIVING THE LESSON

- Believe that you deserve to be happy.
- Know that you deserve to be happy.
- Take action.
- Repeat. Every. Day.

FINAL THOUGHTS

Real change, enduring change, happens one step at a time.

– *Ruth Bader Ginsburg*

We hope this book will inspire you to begin your own happiness practice. As you do, remember Justice Ginsburg's words. Justice Ginsburg was speaking about societal change, but her words apply to us, as individuals. You cannot jump to the top of a mountain. You must take one step at a time.

Keep this in mind, too. There will be times when you may feel like you are off track. You may even feel like you're moving backward. When this happens—and it will—don't beat yourself up. Treat yourself with the kindness and compassion that you would extend to a dear friend. You are worth it. Then, take another step forward.

Although we've been told that happiness is simply a choice, it's not that easy. As we said at the beginning of this book, you can't simply flip a switch and feel happy. But you can take that first step. Those steps add up.

We shall not cease from exploration
And the end of all our exploring
Will be to arrive where we started
And know the place for the first time.

– *T.S. Eliot*

Here's to the journey!

ABOUT THE AUTHORS

NORA RIVA BERGMAN, JD

Nora is dedicated to helping attorneys create the lives and law practices they dreamed of when they were in law school. A licensed attorney since 1992, she appreciates the frustrations that lawyers experience every day, and she is committed to helping them improve their professional and personal lives. She is the creator of the *50 Lessons for Lawyers* book series designed to support lawyers throughout every stage of their careers.

After graduating from law school, Nora practiced as an employment law attorney and certified mediator. She has served as an adjunct professor at Stetson University College of Law and the University of South Florida. Nora has also served as the executive director of the St. Petersburg Bar Association in St. Petersburg, Florida. She has presented at conferences for the American Bar Association, The Florida Bar, and other national and regional bar associations and legal organizations.

Nora brings a unique background to her work as a law firm coach and consultant. She began playing the piano when she was five years old, but gave up piano for the guitar when she was ten and has been playing guitar ever since. After graduating from high school, she worked as professional musician and singer before attending college and through her first year of law school.

In addition to her law degree, Nora is certified in the Conflict Dynamics Profile developed by the Center for Conflict Dynamics at Eckerd College to help individuals and organizations learn to deal constructively with conflict. Nora is also a graduate of Villanova University's Lean Six Sigma Program and is certified in both DISC and EQ through Target Training International.

Nora received an undergraduate degree in journalism, *summa cum laude*, from the University of South Florida and her JD, *cum laude*, from Stetson University College of Law, where she was a member of the law review and served as a mentor for incoming students.

Nora is an avid Peloton rider and has logged over 14,000 miles since she got her bike in 2018. She lives in Tarpon Springs, Florida, with her wife, Jan, and their beautiful Samoyed, Quinn.

CHELSY A. CASTRO, JD, MA, AM, LCSW

Chelsy is CEO and Founder of Castro Jacobs Psychotherapy and Consulting (CJPC), a firm specializing in lawyer well-being. A lawyer turned psychotherapist, consultant, and performance coach, Chelsy, combines her clinical training and legal experience to counsel individuals, groups, and the organizations they work for on how to achieve their goals in healthy and productive ways. Chelsy's publications and continuing legal education trainings focus on science-based skills and strategies for improving performance and increasing well-being in high pressure professions.

After graduating with her simultaneous Juris Doctor and Master of Arts in International Politics from American University, Chelsy practiced law as a multilingual attorney in the field of international regulatory compliance. Motivated both by her own and her colleagues' experiences in the legal field, Chelsy earned her clinical degree at the University of Chicago and shifted her focus from practicing law to helping other lawyers practice happier, healthier, and more productively. Prior to launching CJPC, she designed, developed, and managed clinical and outreach programs and provided psychotherapy for lawyers, judges, and law students as a director and clinician for the Lawyers' Assistance Program.

Chelsy's approach as a psychotherapist, consultant, and performance coach has been informed by both her professional and personal experiences. A child of Cuban immigrants and a former salsa dance instructor, Chelsy lends a unique first-hand understanding of how personal background and family culture influence how and why we pursue our professional ambitions.

Through CJPC, Chelsy has the privilege of serving amazing lawyers and organizations from around the world. She regularly conducts trainings for international corporations and presents at both national and international conferences. Her experience presenting scienced-based well-being and productivity training for lawyers also includes her work with the American Bar Association, the New York State Bar Association, and the Illinois Bar Association among many other professional organizations.

WORKS CITED

Achor, Shawn. *The Happiness Advantage: The Seven Principles of Positive Psychology That Fuel Success and Performance at Work.* Crown Business, 2010.

Albert, Linda. "Keeping Legal Minds Intact: Mitigating Compassion Fatigue." *Wisconsin Lawyers Assistance Program* (April 24, 2015). https://wisatj.org/avoiding-compassion-fatigue

Allen, Summer. "Why Is Gratitude So Hard for Some People?" *Greater Good Magazine* (May 10, 2018). https://greatergood.berkeley.edu/article/item/why_is_gratitude_so_hard_for_some_people

Allen, David. *Getting Things Done: The Art of Stress-Free Productivity.* Penguin Books, 2002.

Aragón, Oriana, Margaret Clark, Rebecca L Dyer, and John Bargh. "Dimorphous expressions of positive emotion: displays of both care and aggression in response to cute stimuli." *Psychological Sciences,* 26(3): 259 – 73, (January, 2015). https://journals.sagepub.com/doi/10.1177/0956797614561044

Bauer, Amber. "Why Do Pets Make Us Feel Better?" *Cancer.Net Blog* (April 23, 2015). (https://www.cancer.net/blog/2015-04/why-do-pets-make-us-feel-better

Becker, Joshua. *The More of Less: Finding the Life You Want Under Everything You Own*. WaterBrook Press, 2016.

Becker, Joshua. "The One Sentence You Need Each Day to Set Your Intention." *Becoming Minimalist* (September 23, 2019). https://www.becomingminimalist.com/intention-setting/

Ben-Shahar, Tal. *The Pursuit of Perfect: How to Stop Chasing Perfection and Start Living a Richer, Happier Life.* McGraw-Hill, 2009.

Bhattacharya, Sudip, Abu Bashar, Abhay Srivastava, and Amarjeet Singh. "*NOMOPHOBIA: NO MObile PHone PHOBIA.*" *Journal of Family Medicine and Primary Care*, 8(4), (April 2019): 1297–1300. https://www.ncbi.nlm.nih.gov/pmc/articles/PMC6510111/

Blatchford, Emily. "Writing By Hand Improves Your Memory, Experts Say." *Huffpost* (July 14, 2016). https://www.huffpost.com/entry/writing-by-hand-improves-your-memory-experts-say_n_61087608e4b0999d2084f66b

Blount, Sally, and Sophie Leroy. "The Synchronous Leader: How Social Synchrony Impacts Teams" *Human Synergistics International* (November 29, 2016).
https://www.humansynergistics.com/blog/culture-university/details/culture-university/2016/11/29/the-synchronous-leader-how-social-synchrony-impacts-teams

Boyes, Alice. "6 Benefits of an Uncluttered Space." *Psychology Today* (February 12, 2018). https://www.psychologytoday.com/us/blog/in-practice/201802/6-benefits-uncluttered-space

Bradberry, Travis. "Why You Should Spend Your Money on Experiences, Not Things." *Forbes* (August 9, 2016).
https://www.forbes.com/sites/travisbradberry/2016/08/09/

why-you-should-spend-your-money-on-experiences-not-things/?sh=55205c436520

Bratman, Gregory, et al. "Nature and mental health: An ecosystem service perspective." *Science Advances* (July 19, 2019). https://www.science.org/doi/10.1126/sciadv.aax0903#pill-R33

Brennan, Dan. "Mental Health Benefits of Decluttering." *WebMD.com* (October 25, 2021). https://www.webmd.com/mental-health/mental-health-benefits-of-decluttering#:~:text=If%20you're%20looking%20for,for%20a%20more%20relaxed%20mind.

Brown, Brené. *Daring Greatly: How the Courage to Be Vulnerable Transforms the Way We Live, Love, Parent, and Lead.* Penguin Random House, 2012.

Brown, Stuart. *How it Shapes the Brain, Opens the Imagination, and Invigorates the Soul.* New York: Avery, 2009.

Buchanan, Bree, and James Coyle. "National Task Force on Lawyer Well-Being: Creating a Movement To Improve Well-Being in the Legal Profession." *American Bar Association* (August 14, 2017). https://www.americanbar.org/content/dam/aba/images/abanews/ThePathToLawyerWellBeingReportRevFINAL.pdf

Chambers, Anne. "Judges and Compassion Fatigue: What Is It and What to Do About It" *The Missouri Bar.* https://mobar.org/site/content/Articles/Well_Being/Judges_and_Compassion_Fatigue__What_Is_It_and_What_to_Do_About_It.aspx

Chemin, Anne. "Handwriting vs Typing: Is the Pen Still Mightier Than the Keyboard?" *The Guardian* (December 14, 2016). https://www.theguardian.com/science/2014/dec/16/cognitive-benefits-handwriting-decline-typing

Cho, Jeena, and Karen Gifford. *The Anxious Lawyer: An 8-Week Guide to a Happier, Saner Law Practice Using Meditation.* American Bar Association, 2016.

Clio, "2018 Legal Trends Report." *Themis Solutions* (2018). https://www.clio.com/resources/legal-trends/2018-report/

Cooper, Robert. *The Other 90% - How to Unlock Your Vast Untapped Potential for Leadership and Life*. Crown Business, 2002.

Covey, Stephen. *The 7 Habits of Highly Effective People.* Simon & Schuster, 2004.

Craig, Heather. "What are the Benefits of Music Therapy?" *PositivePsychology.com* (June 12, 2021). https://positivepsychology.com/music-therapy-benefits/

Csikszentmihalyi, Mihaly. *Flow: The Psychology of Optimal Experience.* Harper Perennial Modern Classics, 2008.

Darwin, Charles. *The Expression of the Emotions in Man and Animals.* London: John Murray, 1872.

Duckworth, Angela. *Grit: The Power of Passion and Perseverance.* Scribner, 2016.

Duhigg, Charles. *The Power of Habit: Why We Do What We Do in Life and Business.* Random House Trade Paperbacks, 2014.

Dutton, Judy. "Make Your Bed, Change Your Life?" *Psychology Today* (August 16, 2012). https://www.psychologytoday.com/us/blog/brain-candy/201208/make-your-bed-change-your-life

Editorial Staff. "16 Science-Backed Reasons Adopting a Dog Could Be Good for Your Heart." *American Heart Association* (January 31, 2020). https://www.heart.org/en/healthy-living/healthy-bond-for-life-pets/a-dog-could-be-good-for-your-heart

Editorial Staff. "The Friend Who Keeps You Young." *Johns Hopkins Medicine* (2022). https://www.hopkinsmedicine.org/health/wellness-and-prevention/the-friend-who-keeps-you-young

Epstein, Sarah. "It's OK Not to Feel Grateful Right Now." *Psychology Today* (March 31, 2020). https://www.psychologytoday.com/us/blog/between-the-generations/202003/its-ok-not-feel-grateful-right-now

Ferrari, Joseph. *Still Procrastinating: The No Regrets Guide to Getting It Done.* John Wiley & Sons, 2010.

Figley, Charles. *Compassion Fatigue: Coping with Secondary Traumatic Stress Disorder in Those Who Treat the Traumatized.* Charles R. Figley ed., 1995.

Flores, David, Martin Reimann, Raquel Castaño, and Alberto Lopez. "If I indulge first, I will eat less overall: The unexpected interaction effect of indulgence and presentation order on consumption." *Journal of Experimental Psychology: Applied*, 25(2), (2019): 162–176. https://psycnet.apa.org/record/2019-04355-001?doi=1

Fredrickson, Barbara. *Positivity: Groundbreaking Research Reveals How to Embrace the Hidden Strength of Positive Emotions, Overcome Negativity, and Thrive.* Crown Archetype, 2008.

Global Wellness Institute Staff. "What is wellness?" *Global Wellness Institute* (February 1, 2022). https://globalwellnessinstitute.org/what-is-wellness/

Goleman, Daniel. *Emotional Intelligence.* Bantam Books, 2006.

Goleman, Daniel, Richard Boyatzis, and Annie McKee. *Primal Leadership: Unleashing the Power of Emotional Intelligence.* Harvard Business Review Press, 2013.

Gordon, Ilanit. "What is Synchrony and Why is it Important." *Psychology Today* (June 12, 2020). https://www.psychologytoday.com/us/blog/the-biology-bonding/202006/what-is-synchrony-and-why-is-it-important

Grăcanin, Asmir, Lauren Bylsma, and J. J. M. Vingerhoets. "Is crying a self-soothing behavior?" *Frontiers in Psychology,* 5(502), (May 2014). https://doi.org/10.3389/fpsyg.2014.00502

Grady, Anne. *Mind Over Moment: Harness the Power of Resilience.* Anne Grady, 2020.

Grant, Michael. *A Short History of Classical Civilization.* London: Weidenfeld and Nicolson, 1991.

Ha, Thu-Huong. "5 Exercises to Help You Build more Empathy." *We Humans* (March 16, 2021). https://ideas.ted.com/5-exercises-to-help-you-build-more-empathy/

Hanson, Rick. *Just One Thing: Developing a Buddha Brain One Simple Practice at a Time.* New Harbinger Publications, 2011.

Hanson, Rick. "Just One Thing: Let It Go." *Greater Good Magazine* (January 5, 2015). https://greatergood.berkeley.edu/article/item/just_one_thing_let_it_go

Hanson, Rick, and Forrest Hanson. *Resilient: How to Grow an Unshakable Core of Calm, Strength, and Happiness.* Harmony Books, 2018.

Harvard Health Publishing. "A Flexible Way to Stretch." *Harvard* (May 1, 2019).

Hay, Louise. *101 Power Thoughts.* Hay House, 2004.

Hayes, Steven. *Get out of Your Mind and Into Your Life.* New Harbinger Publications, 2005.

Heshmat, Shahram. "Social Benefits of Synchronization." *Psychology Today* (December 31, 2021). https://www.psychologytoday.com/us/blog/science-choice/202112/social-benefits-synchronization

Hsu, Andrea. "Iceland Cut Its Work Week And Found Greater Happiness And No Loss In Productivity." *NPR* (July 6,

2021). https://www.npr.org/2021/07/06/1013348626/iceland-finds-major-success-moving-to-shorter-work-week

Hutchinson, Hilery. *10-Minute Stretching: Simple Exercises to Build Flexibility into Your Daily Routine.* Rockridge Press, 2021.

James, William. "What Is an Emotion?" *Mind,* 9(34), (1884): 188-205. http://www.jstor.org/stable/2246769.

Jeffers, Susan. *Feel the Fear and Do It Anyway: Dynamic Techniques for Turning Fear, Indecision and Anger into Power, Action and Love.* Jeffers Press, 2007.

Jones, Jeffrey. "In U.S., 40% Get Less Than Recommended Amount of Sleep." *Gallup* (December 19, 2013). http://www.gallup.com/poll/166553/less-recommended-amount-sleep.aspx

Kawasaki, Guy. *Enchantment: The Art of Changing Hearts, Minds, and Actions.* New York: Portfolio/Penguin, 2011.

Keeva, Steven. *Transforming Practices: Finding Joy and Satisfaction in the Legal Life.* American Bar Association, 1999.

Kondō, Marie. *The Life-Changing Magic of Tidying Up: The Japanese Art of Decluttering and Organizing.* Clarkson Potter/Ten Speed, 2014.

Kondo, Marie, and Scott Sonenshein. *Joy at Work: Organizing Your Professional Life*. Little, Brown Spark, 2020.

Krieger, Lawrence. "*What Makes Lawyers Lawyers Happy? A Data-Driven Prescription to Redefine Professional Success.*" *George Washington Law Review,* 83, (2015): 554 – 627. https://ir.law.fsu.edu/articles/94/

Krznaric, Roman. *Empathy: Why It Matters and How to Get It.* Penguin Group, 2014.

Kumar, Amit, Matthew Killingsworth, and Thomas Gilovich. "Waiting for Merlot: Anticipatory Consumption of Experiential and Material

Purchases." *Psychological Science,* vol. 25 issue 10 (2014): 192 – 1931. https://doi.org/10.1177/0956797614546556

Lindberg, Sara. "How Does Your Environment Affect Your Mental Health?" *Very Well Mind* (Updated January 25, 2021). https://www.verywellmind.com/how-your-environment-affects-your-mental-health-5093687

Longcamp, Marieke, Marie-Therese Zerbato-Poudou, and Jean-Luc Velay. "The influence of writing practice on letter recognition in preschool children: a comparison between handwriting and typing." *National Library of Medicine* (January 4, 2005). https://pubmed.ncbi.nlm.nih.gov/15823243/

Luks, Allan, and Peggy Payne. *The Healing Power of Doing Good: The Health and Spiritual Benefits of Helping Others.* Fawcett, 1992.

Lyubomirsky, Sonja. *The How of Happiness: A Scientific Approach to Getting the Life You Want.* Penguin Books, 2008.

Matthews, Donna. "Empathy: Where Kindness, Compassion, and Happiness Begin." *Psychology Today* (October 31. 2019). https://www.psychologytoday.com/us/blog/going-beyond-intelligence/201910/empathy-where-kindness-compassion-and-happiness-begin

Mayo Clinic Staff. "Stress relief from laughter? It's no joke." *Mayo Clinic* (April 5, 2019). https://www.mayoclinic.org/healthy-lifestyle/stress-management/in-depth/stress-relief/art-20044456

Mayo Clinic Staff. "Friendships: Enrich your life and improve your health." *Mayo Clinic* (January 12, 2022). https://www.mayoclinic.org/healthy-lifestyle/adult-health/in-depth/friendships/art-20044860

McGonigal, Kelly. *The Willpower Instinct: How Self-Control Works, Why It Matters, and What You Can Do To Get More of It.* Avery Trade, 2013.

McGraw, Peter, and Joel Warner. *The Humor Code: A Global Search for What Makes Things Funny.* Simon & Schuster, 2014.

Mckee, Alia, and Tim Walker. "State of Friendship in America Report." *Lifeboat*. (February 2015). http://www.getlifeboat.com/report

McRaven, William. *Make Your Bed: Little Things That Can Change Your Life . . . and Maybe the World.* Grand Central Publishing, 2017.

Medina, John. *Brain Rules: 12 Principles for Surviving and Thriving at Work, Home and School.* Pear Press, 2008.

Merlo, Kelsey, et al. "A qualitative study of daydreaming episodes at work." *Journal of Business and Psychology,* 35, (2020): 203–222. https://doi.org/10.1007/s10869-018-9611-4

Newman, Kira. "Six Ways Happiness Is Good for Your Health." *Greater Good Magazine* (July 28, 2015). https://greatergood.berkeley.edu/article/item/six_ways_happiness_is_good_for_your_health

Oettingen, Gabriele. *Rethinking Positive Thinking: Inside the New Science of Motivation.* Penguin Group, 2014.

Pendell, Ryan. "Wellness vs. Wellbeing: What's the Difference?" *Gallup* (March 22, 2021). https://www.gallup.com/workplace/340202/wellness-wellbeing-difference.aspx

Penn, Joanna. "The Pen is Mightier Than the Keyboard: Advantages of Longhand Over Laptop Note Taking." *The Journalist's Resource* (July 30, 2014). https://journalistsresource.org/education/longhand-versus-laptop-note-taking/

Perry, Bruce, and Maia Szalavitz. *Born for Love.* HarperCollins, 2010.

Pfeffer, Jeffrey. *Dying for a Paycheck: How Modern Management Harms Employee Health and Company Performance – and What We Can Do About It.* Harper Business, 2018.

Pinker, Steven. *How the Mind Works.* W. W. Norton & Company, 1997.

Piterelli, Monica Buchanan. "Mental escape' pictures actually relieve stress. Here's what they look like." CNBC (March 31, 2020). https://www.

cnbc.com/2020/03/31/mental-vacations-and-travel-photos-relieve-stress.html

Poswolsky, Adam Smiley. *Friendship in the Age of Loneliness: An Optimist's Guide to Connection.* Running Press, Hachette Book Group, 2021.

Preiss, David, Diego Cosmelli and James Kaufman. *Creativity and the Wandering Mind: Spontaneous and Controlled Cognition.* Academic Press, 2020.

Project Wellness Staff. "Volunteering and Mental Wellness." *Project Wellness* (2021). https://projecthelping.org/benefits-of-volunteering/

Proyer, René. "A new structural model for the study of adult playfulness: Assessment and exploration of an understudied individual differences variable." *Personality and Individual Differences*, 108 (April 2017): 113 – 122. https://doi.org/10.1016/j.paid.2016.12.011

Rao, Srikumar. *Happiness at Work: Be Resilient, Motivated, and Successful – No Matter What.* McGraw Hill, 2010.

Razzetti, Gustavo. "How to Let Go of the Past." *Psychology Today* (February 13, 2020). https://www.psychologytoday.com/us/blog/the-adaptive-mind/202002/how-let-go-the-past

Rector, Clark. "Ecopsychology: The Study of Your Relationship to the Natural World." HealthyPsych (April 22, 2015). https://healthypsych.com/ecopsychology-the-study-of-your-relationship-to-the-natural-world/

Revell, Timothy. "Can a shorter working week make us happier?" *Acuity* (December 1, 2018). https://www.acuitymag.com/business/can-a-shorter-working-week-make-us-happier

Rhodes, Maura. "5 Ways Our Pets Make Us Happy." *Livehappy.com* (April 15, 2015). https://www.livehappy.com/animals/5-ways-our-pets-make-us-happy

Robbins, Mike. "How to Bring Your Whole Self to Work." *Greater Good*

Magazine (September 19, 2018). https://greatergood.berkeley.edu/article/item/how_to_bring_your_whole_self_to_work

Robbins, Jim. "Ecopsychology: How Immersion in Nature Benefits Your Health." *YaleEnvironment360* (January 9, 2020). https://e360.yale.edu/features/ecopsychology-how-immersion-in-nature-benefits-your-health

Robbins, Mike. *Bring Your Whole Self to Work.* Hay House, 2018.

Robinson, Gray. "Preventing Compassion Fatigue: When Lawyers Care Too Much." *Attorney at Work* (August 12, 2021). https://www.attorneyat-work.com/preventing-compassion-fatigue/

Rossman, Jeffrey. T*he Mind Body Solution: The Breakthrough Drug-Free Program for Lasting Relief from Depression.* Rodale Books, 2010.

Rountree, Sage. *The Athlete's Guide to Recovery: Rest, Relax, and Restore for Peak Performance.* VeloPress, 2011.

Rowling, J., K. "The Fringe Benefits of Failure, and the Importance of Imagination." *The Harvard Gazette* (June 5, 2008). https://news.harvard.edu/gazette/story/2008/06/text-of-j-k-rowling-speech/

St. John, Bonnie, and Allen Haines. *Micro-Resilience: Minor Shifts for Major Boosts in Focus, Drive, and Energy.* Center Street, 2017.

Seligman, Martin. *Authentic Happiness: Using the New Positive Psychology to Realize Your Potential for Lasting Fulfillment.* Free Press, 2022.

Seligman, Martin. *Flourish: A Visionary New Understanding of Happiness and Well-being.* Atria Books, 2011.

Shi, Diana. "I tried making a 'to-don't list' instead of a to-do list. Here's what I learned." *Fast Company* (April 6, 2021). https://www.fastcompany.com/90617576/i-tried-making-a-to-dont-list-instead-of-a-to-do-list-heres-what-i-learned

Siegle, Steve. "The Art of Kindness." *Mayo Clinic Health.* (May 29, 2020). https://www.mayoclinichealthsystem.org/hometown-health/

speaking-of-health/the-art-of-kindness

Smith, Jeremy Adam, et al. *The Gratitude Project: How the Science of Thankfulness Can Rewire Our Brains for Resilience, Optimism, and the Greater Good.* Oakland, CA: New Harbinger Publications, Inc, 2020.

Stamm, Beth Hudnall. "Compassion Fatigue." *North Carolina Lawyer Assistance Program*

Steckl, Carrie. "Empathy: It's About Happiness, Too." *American Addiction Centers* https://www.mentalhelp.net/blogs/empathy-it-s-about-happiness-too/

Suttie, Jill. "How Nature Can Make You Kinder, Happier, and More Creative." *Greater Good Magazine* (March 2, 2016). https://greatergood.berkeley.edu/article/item/how_nature_makes_you_kinder_happier_more_creative

Thibodeaux, Wanda. "Your Happiness Isn't Related to Your Work Hours, According to a New Report." *INC Magazine* (December 17, 2018). https://greatergood.berkeley.edu/article/item/would_working_less_make_you_happier

Tierney, John, and Roy Baumeister. *The Power of Bad: How the Negativity Effect Rules and How We Can Rule It.* Penguin Press, 2019.

Time Magazine Staff. "Health and Happiness: Try New Things." *Time Magazine* http://content.time.com/time/specials/2007/article/0,28804,1631176_1630611_1630586,00.html

Tripathy, Koushik. "Computer Vision Syndrome (Digital Eye Strain)." *American Academy of Ophthalmology* (March 17, 2022). https://eyewiki.org/Computer_Vision_Syndrome_(Digital_Eye_Strain)#Symptoms.5B2.5D.5B4.5D

Tugend, Alina. "Praise is Fleeting, but Brickbats We Recall." *New York Times* (March 23, 2012).

https://www.nytimes.com/2012/03/24/your-money/why-people-remember-negative-events-more-than-positive-ones.html

UCHealth Staff. "Rest and recovery are critical for an athlete's physiological and psychological well-being." *Journal Advocate* (February 10, 2022). https://www.journal-advocate.com/2022/02/10/rest-and-recovery-are-critical-for-an-athletes-physiological-and-psychological-well-being/

Verywell Mind. "What Is the Negativity Bias?" *Very Well Mind* (April 29, 2020). https://www.verywellmind.com/negative-bias-4589618

Walker, Mathew. *Why We Sleep: Unlocking the Power of Sleep and Dreams.* Scribner, 2017.

Warkentin, Shahrzad. "Want to Eat Healthier? Science Says Go Ahead & Have Dessert—First." *Tiny Beans* (March 5, 2019).

Weir, Kirsten. "The Exercise Effect." *American Psychological Association* (December 10, 2011). https://www.apa.org/monitor/2011/12/exercise

Westgate, Erin. "Why we're so bad at daydreaming, and how to fix it." *University of Florida News* (March 4, 2021). https://news.ufl.edu/2021/03/daydreaming/

Wollen, Malia. "How to Get In Sync With Someone." *New York Times* (November 24, 2020). https://www.nytimes.com/2020/11/24/magazine/how-to-get-in-sync-with-someone.html

Wong, Brian. "How Learning a New Skill Helps Your Mind Grow Stronger." *Inc. Magazine* (December 29, 2017). https://www.inc.com/brian-wong/how-learning-a-new-skill-helps-your-mind-grow-stronger.html

Wong, Kapo, Alan Chan, and S. C. Ngan. "The Effect of Long Working Hours and Overtime on Occupational Health: A Meta-Analysis of Evidence from 1998 to 2018." *International Journal of Environmental*

Research and Public Health, 16(12), (June 2019). https://doi.org/10.3390/ijerph16122102

Wong, Kristin. "How to Add More Play to your Grown-Up Life, Even Now." *New York Times*, (August 14, 2020). https://www.nytimes.com/2020/08/14/smarter-living/adults-play-work-life-balance.html

World Health Organization and the International Labour Organization. "Long working hours increasing deaths from heart disease and stroke: WHO, ILO" *WHO and ILO.* (May 17, 2021). https://www.who.int/news/item/17-05-2021-long-working-hours-increasing-deaths-from-heart-disease-and-stroke-who-ilo

Zaki, Jamil. *The War for Kindness: Building Empathy in a Fractured World.* Broadway Books, 2019.

Zaraska, Marta. *Growing Young: How Friendship, Optimism, and Kindness Can Help You Live to 100.* (Random House, 2020)

Made in the USA
Monee, IL
09 May 2023

33230945R00132